For Lennon,
With all our best.
Enjoy!

Sally O'Sullivan

Chapter 1.

George Morton – Prepares for a trip to Florida – The vessel sails – Sea Sickness – A Steamer ashore – Rescue of Passengers – Gulf Stream – A Storm – arrival at Savannah – A walk in Savannah

George Morton the hero of this story, was a lad of seventeen years of age. His Parents had always resided in the great City of New York; but George had been at a boarding school in the country for several years. His Father had died of Consumption about a year before the commencement of our tale; and his Mother feeling lonely, as she had but one other child, had decided that George should live at home. He had therefore been attending a school in the city, for a year and becoming very much interested in his studies, he had applied himself closely to them. He was tall for his age and rather slender. In the Spring George took a bad cold, and had a cough, during the whole Summer and Fall. His Mother became alarmed about his health, and consulted her family physician, who advised George to give up his studies for a time, and to take more exercise in the open air. He thought too, that a trip to the South, during the extreme cold weather, would be of service to him.

George had an Uncle who was very fond of him. Since his Fathers death, Uncle James, who was a Batchelor, had lived with his sister. Mrs. Morton told him of the advice the physician had given, and asked him what he thought in regard to it. Uncle James said "that he had thought of spending the coming winter in Florida himself, to avoid the attacks of rheumatism to which he was subject, and that he would willingly take George with him, and thought it would be an excellent thing for him".

Mrs. Morton felt that it would be a trial to part with him, but she was willing to do it, if there was any probability of its being beneficial to him. It was therefore arranged, that Uncle James and George, should go to Florida, in the month of December

A Trip to Florida for Health and Sport:

The Lost 1855 Novel of
Cyrus Parkhurst Condit

Edited and with an Introduction by
Maurice O'Sullivan and Wenxian Zhang

A Trip to Florida for Health and Sport:

The Lost 1855 Novel of Cyrus Parkhurst Condit

Edited and with an Introduction by Maurice O'Sullivan and Wenxian Zhang

Copyright 2009

Published by the Florida Historical Society Press

ISBN 10: 1-886104-36-0

ISBN 13: 978-1-886104-36-5

Cover Photograph by Michelle Webb

The Florida Historical Society Press

435 Brevard Avenue

Cocoa, FL 32922

www.myfloridahistory.org/fhspress

100 000 000 000 000
RESERVE BANK OF ZIMBABWE
100 000 000 000 000
I promise to pay
the bearer on demand
ONE HUNDRED
TRILLION
DOLLARS
for the Reserve Bank of Zimbabwe
Dr. G. Gono
Governor
100 000 000 000 000
HARARE 2008
AA1943449
AA1943449

100 000 000 000 000

RESERVE BANK OF ZIMBABWE

100 000 000 000 000

WE DEDICATE THIS BOOK TO

KAREN DU AND SUSAN M. FOWLER

温故而知新 - 孔子

Study the past, if you want to divine the future.

Confucius

Table of Contents

INTRODUCTION

While conducting a summer inventory in the Archives and Special Collections at Rollins College, Wenxian Zhang, the college's archivist, discovered a rare manuscript in the school's Florida Collection. It consists of an unpublished novel about a young man's winter visit to Florida. Apparently written by Cyrus Parkhurst Condit (1830 – 1861), it was one of many gifts to Rollins from Frederick Dau, an editor, collector, and the author of *Florida: Old and New* (1934). Based on internal evidence, Condit's biography and historical events, we have concluded that the manuscript was probably written in 1855.

The novel tells the story of George Morton, a seventeen year old New Yorker who travels one December to Florida for his health. While most of the narrative focuses on Welaka, a small town 55 miles south of Jacksonville, and the adjacent Lake George region, it also includes visits to St. Augustine, Enterprise, Mellonville (now Sanford) and Silver Glen Springs, as well as hunting, fishing and camping trips along the state's rivers and lakes.

The manuscript's importance stems both from its date, which makes it one of the state's first novels, and from its detailed portrait of ordinary life along the St. Johns River in the early 1850s. In describing how the handful of Welaka residents and the farmers who surrounded them worked and socialized, married and worshipped, hunted and fished, Condit has made a rich contribution to our understanding of antebellum Florida. The story's incidents and descriptions are so circumstantial in detail that they appear clearly based on first-hand experience or taken from familiar local anecdote. It is the book's record of those distinctively Floridian customs, the large and small events of day-by-day life, that makes it so valuable.

Although Florida has the oldest, most diverse, and richest literary tradition in North America, by the mid-1850s only ten novels had been set in the state. Despite that small number, a majority of them were the work of the country's most important writers. Like Florida's first novelist, François-René, the vicomte de Chateaubriand, whose enormously popular 1801 story of a doomed romance among the Native Americans in La Florida, *Atala*, influenced French literature for generations, most of those early novelists look either to the past or to the complex diversity of the region's population for tales that mix adventure and romance, legend and history.

Two bestselling authors, Joseph Holt Ingraham and Ned Buntline, wrote potboilers about Spanish pirates ravaging the Florida coasts, *Rafael; or, The Twice Condemned* (1845) and *The Red Revenger; or, The Pirate King of Florida* (1847), while the iconic James Fenimore Cooper published *Jack Tier; or, The Florida Reef* (1848), a sea yarn about a modern pirate during the Mexican-American War. The prolific Ned Buntline, who produced over 400 novels during his colorful life, also wrote a story about the bloody sixteenth-century conflict between Spanish and French Huguenot colonists, *Matanzas* (1848). South Carolina's William Gilmore Simms, considered by Edgar Allen Poe a greater writer than Cooper, returned to the same period in *Vasconselos* (1853), a more thoughtful exploration of the clash of cultures between Cuba and Florida, Europeans and natives, while the antebellum South's most popular writer, Caroline Lee Whiting Hentz, used her *Marcus Warland; or, The Long Moss Spring* (1852) for a defense of slavery and plantation life.

Unlike those books, or the handful of other early Florida novels, *A Trip to Florida for Health and Sport* is a quietly domestic account of everyday life in the new state of Florida. The peaceful worlds of Welaka and Lake George offer adventures, but solely for those who choose to enter the woods in search of deer and bear. Only Francis Robert Goulding's *Robert and Harold; or, The Young Marooners on the Florida Coast* (1853) has a similar story of teenagers and pre-teens learning new skills in a new environment, but Goulding's work, set decades earlier in 1830, focuses on the ways four devout young Georgians impose their Presbyterian values on the environment they find rather than the ways that environment alters them.

Condit's novel is closer to the literature that followed the Civil War than to these first Florida novels. In 1869 Ledyard Bill's *A Winter in Florida* sparked an interest in the state's climate, flora, fauna, history, culture and customs. The popularity of Bill's travel book, which had four editions by the end of the following year, inspired the publication of works like Harriet Beecher Stowe's *Palmetto Leaves* (1873), Sidney Lanier's *Florida* (1875), and Silvia Sunshine's *Petals Plucked from Sunny Climes* (1879). John Muir's *A Thousand-Mile Walk to the Gulf* (written in 1867 but first published in 1916) and Lafcadio Hearn's "Floridian Reveries" (1911) are later notable examples of this tradition.

These works all echo an older Florida tradition of ecoliterature, which began with such Spanish and French accounts as Peter Martyr D'Anghiera's *De Orbe Novo Decades* (1530), Alvar Núñez Cabeza de Vaca's *Los Naufragios* (1555), and Jean Ribaut's *The Whole and True Discoverye of Terra Florida* (1563). In the Eighteenth Century, British naturalists like Mark Catesby (1731-43), William Roberts (1763), and Bernard Romans (1775) began using scientific principles to define the region's geography, flora and fauna; and as soon as the revolution ended, American naturalists started exploring their Southern neighbor. Thomas Hutchins' *An Historical Narrative and Topographical Description of Louisiana and West Florida* appeared in 1784; and in 1791 William Bartram finally published his *Travels*, an account of a three year trip he took to Florida, Georgia and Alabama.

Although Bartram's *Travels* may well be the single most influential book ever written about the state—many writers who never actually visited Florida, like Chateaubriand and even British romantic poets like Samuel Taylor Coleridge, borrowed freely from its imagery—the only edition of the work to appear during the nineteenth century was published in French and, curiously enough, in the same city, Paris, and year, 1801, as the state's first novel, *Atala*. The last of the important studies of Florida's environment before the Civil War was the second volume of John James Audubon's *Ornithological Biography* (1834), which redefined the way the world saw Florida's wildlife.

While those accounts, especially the latter ones, offered relatively precise descriptions of the southernmost state's environment, it was fiction which excited the nation's imagination. At about the same time as Hearn's "Reveries" in 1911, publishers began offering adventure series for teenagers. And the many popular examples of what we call today Young Adult literature—the M's alone include the *Motor Boat Club*, the *Motorboat Boys*, the *Motor Maids*, and the *Mystery Boys*—almost always included a volume about the group's adventures in Florida.

A Trip to Florida for Health and Sport foreshadows both these stories of young Northerners braving the southern frontier and the large body of post-Civil War travel literature about Florida. Condit clearly has multiple goals in mind, goals which, at times, conflict. Although the book is primarily an adventure story, the author interrupts that story at the beginning and end to give what read like a tourist guide's historical and descriptive accounts of Savannah and St. Augustine. And in the tradition of Bartram and Audubon, he also suspends his narrative occasionally for short naturalist disquisitions on everything from the varieties of oranges to the state's squirrels and insects.

Much of the novel's value stems from showing the state's lush but challenging environment almost two decades before it became a popular tourist destination, before the railroads, grand hotels, and eventually campgrounds and motels would transform it into a still exotic but far more accessible frontier that would attract

Thomas Edison, Henry Ford, Ernest Hemingway, the tin can tourists of the 1920s and finally even Nancy Drew in *The Clue of the Black Keys* (1951).

George Morton's Florida is still raw and unpackaged. Excursions need to be planned, occasionally fail and often pose genuine risks. His first attempt to visit Silver Glen Spring on the west side of Lake George in Chapter V shows how precarious travel in antebellum Florida was. (Note that the novel regularly calls Silver Glen Spring "Silver Spring.") Since the state had few roads, its rivers served as the primary highways. While steamboats and barges connected the major towns, local travel, as George soon found, required not only the generosity of those who owned boats and horses but the cooperation of nature.

Although a significant improvement in transportation would not occur until after the Civil War, its foundation was actually laid at the time the novel was written. In 1855 the state legislature passed an Internal Improvement Act, which offered public land to investors, especially those interested in transportation. But the full benefit of that act did not appear until decades later when Henry Plant and Henry Flagler used it to build railroads and a series of great hotels like the Tampa Bay, Ponce de Leon, and Royal Poinciana to encourage wealthy Northerners to winter in Florida.

The stream of early visitors became a flood after the Civil War, especially once railroad tracks crisscrossed the state. As tourism became big business, steamships would provide regular excursions for formally dressed Northerners down the Ocklawaha to Silver Springs. Even Harriet Beecher Stowe, the famous author of *Uncle Tom's Cabin*, who bought a home in Mandarin in 1867, reportedly capitalized on the tourism industry by charging steamship passengers 75 cents to meet the person legends claim Abraham Lincoln once described as "the little woman who started the [Civil] war."

But that world was still far off when George Morton and his Uncle James took a series of steamships from New York to Savannah and then to Fernandina, Jacksonville, Palatka and the small settlement of Welaka. In the early 1850s visitors found a far simpler state. Despite attracting a steadily growing permanent population of settlers, most of those who came for the winter were searching for a healthy environment and a recreational paradise, where men spent much of their time, when not fishing for trout, gar, pickerel, catfish, bream, sheep's head and silver fish, hunting ducks, deer, hog, bear, turkey, osprey, panther and alligator, with occasional practice on varmints like foxes, cat squirrels, black squirrels, catamounts and snakes.

A Trip to Florida for Health and Sport offers a simpler version of the coming of age story than Western classics like *Huckleberry Finn*, *A Portrait of the Artist as a Young Man*, *To Kill a Mockingbird* and *Catcher in the Rye*. Condit has relatively little interest in psychological or emotional development and seems remarkably apolitical; despite the growing tensions between North and South—Florida would be the third state to secede in the Civil War—no one in the book even alludes to them. Instead, George's character and maturity are defined by his skills, by his taking responsibility, and by his increasing respect for nature. As he becomes a more competent and successful hunter, he also finds himself taking a leadership role among his peers and a mentor for younger boys.

Although divided into twelve chapters, Condit really organizes his novel into five clearly defined parts. The first section begins slowly by introducing the ailing George, his concerned mother, and his solicitous Uncle James, who, having planned a trip to Florida for his rheumatism, invites his nephew along. Their voyage from New York to Welaka includes descriptions of storms, the Gulf Stream, Savannah's squares, Fernandina, Jacksonville, the St. Johns, Palatka, and Welaka. Although there are some striking descriptions and a wonderful story of wreckers rescuing passengers from a beached screw steamer, Uncle James's didactic explanations make parts of the opening sound like a school lesson.

Once they arrive in Welaka and George can begin his adventures, the story begins to come alive. He fishes for gar and trout, learns to hunt ducks by firelight, has his first taste of wild oranges, and goes on his first deer hunts. As he makes friends, especially with the rational David, he finds a community as interested in the outdoors as he. This section reaches its climax when George, David, and the young Mr. Hastings visit a legendary figure, the eponymous Mr. Hunter, who entertains them with stories and takes them on a deer hunt. Mr. Hunter's vivid, occasionally droll but very human anecdotes provide the finest material in the novel.

By the time he returns to Welaka from his first visit to the Hunter farm, George has adapted so well to his new environment that he considers it coming "home." Back in Welaka for the middle section of the book, George forms a new friendship with the young captain of a schooner which has come for a shipment of cattle to Guadalupe. The author, clearly recognizing that Mr. Hunter provides a much more effective mentor for George than his uncle had, sends the two-dimensional James off on a business trip for most of the rest of the story. That frees George to grow under a far better role model and to prove himself with adults and peers who have no preconceptions about him. In addition to expanding his adventures into sailing, visiting a logging camp, attempting to visit Silver Glen Spring, and camping along Lake George, he and David spend a day watching their friend Captain Ambler's misadventures in loading cattle onto his schooner and visit Captain Stebbins to see his relics of the late Indian War.

Returning to the Hunters for a long visit, George hears more tales about deer, bears, panthers and alligators and goes on more hunts. Under Mr. Hunter's direction, he becomes more independent and skillful, more judicious and thoughtful. Eventually he comes to understand the creatures he hunts as more than game, as part of a great, interdependent tapestry of life. And, finally, he begins mentoring Mr. Hunter's sons, shows generosity by sharing his venison with his Welaka friends, and demonstrates his maturity by taking time from his adventures to build a road and a fence for the Hunters.

The last section begins with Uncle James's return and includes more trips and hunts, visits to Enterprise and St Augustine. With his newly won maturity, George can cope with a comically inept guide and finally plan a successful trip to Silver Glen Springs. As they return home to New York, George and his uncle appear to have reversed roles, with the younger man taking charge and his uncle quietly following. He left New York a fragile teenager still mourning his father's early death and heavily dependent on his uncle; he returns a happy, healthy, independent young man.

While the novel begins slowly, with the narrator occasionally breaking into his story to warn young boys that running off to sea will not prove as glamorous as it seems or to offer miniature sermons on man's dependence on God, it ends with far more energy, focusing on action rather than admonition. The cautionary, avuncular tone of the opening is reinforced by the presence of George's Uncle James, who prefers offering didactic comments to holding personal conversations. As George earns both skills and a voice, the book gains energy. With Mr. Hunter and his stories, the novel shows what its author is capable of and where he might have taken it if he had been able to revise.

The characters in *A Trip to Florida* love the leisurely pace of Florida life, but not all early Northern visitors shared that appreciation. When Ralph Waldo Emerson, the great nineteenth-century poet and philosopher, visited St. Augustine for his health in 1827, he filled his journal with ironic comments about its citizens: "oldest town of Europeans in North America; full of ruins,--chimneyless houses, lazy people; housekeeping intolerably dear, and bad milk from swamp grass, because all the hay comes from the north. 40 miles from here is nevertheless the richest crop of grass growing untouched. Why? because there is no scythe in St. Augustine, and if there were, no man who knows how to use one" (154).

Although Emerson expressed a deep appreciation for the region's landscape and the city's history, the New Englander who would write memorable essays on "Self Reliance" and "Prudence" found neither quality among Florida's citizens. Unlike Emerson's disapproval of its work ethic, Condit offers an admiring tribute to life in the sunshine and the simple pleasures of both Florida's residents and the antebellum Northern leisure class. Passengers on a steamboat in the St. Johns, for example, can enjoy a morning doing little more than shouting at cranes along the side of the river. And in Welaka, George and his new friends watch or participate in the customs and rituals of everyday Florida life whenever they are not hunting or fishing—or telling stories about hunting and fishing.

George watches as the residents of Welaka protect their town from a forest fire and as his friend Captain Ambler and his crew load a group of unhappy steers into a schooner for shipment north. At the Hunters, he learns about cooperative farming, log rolling, and fence building. He watches as the women use nursing calves to distract wild cows so they can sneak in and milk them. He visits a lumber mill, discovers the natural beauties of lakes and springs, attends religious services with an itinerant preacher, and joins in the festivities at a country wedding.

But most of the novel focuses on the rituals of fishing, hunting and exploring. Those activities consume not only his time and that of most of his companions, but their conversation as well. In fact, in this world men and boys are measured largely by their skill with rod and gun and their ability to turn their adventures into compelling stories. The best people in the story have the best skills and tell the best stories. This is a simpler version of the world later captured by Ernest Hemingway, Zane Grey, Marjorie Kinnan Rawlings and Harry Crews.

By the mid-1850s the Florida George visited had a population which would have just passed 100,000. Even before the United States gained the Spanish colonies of East Florida and West Florida in a treaty signed in 1819 but not ratified until 1821, the territory had attracted settlers, largely from adjacent Southern states. Once Florida became an American territory, those settlers, along with many new ones pouring across the border, began pressuring Washington to open up more land for development by relocating the Seminoles and Miccosukee to the West. Soon after, they began lobbying for statehood, which eventually came in 1845 when Florida became the 27th state, paired with Iowa to preserve the precarious free state/slave state balance.

Even as its population soared—in 1800 the two Spanish colonies of East and West Florida had an estimated 12,000 people—the area remained an exotic destination, with vast tracts of inexpensive land and an astonishing variety of game and sport fish. The 1830 U.S. census—the first to include the new territory—showed 34,730 people in Florida. After that the numbers accelerated rapidly to 54,477 in 1840, 87,445 in 1850 and 140,424 in 1860.

These new residents tended to be far more homogeneous than the area's earlier population. At the beginning of the century, Florida had the most ethnically heterogeneous population in North America, a rich mix of Spanish, British, Minorcans, French Creoles, Canary Islanders, Americans, Africans, other Europeans, and Native Americans. But as more and more Southerners migrated even farther south, many of those groups became curiosities, often marginalized into their own communities. Condit's comments about Romish priests in St. Augustine and the Inquisition reflect some of the comfortable prejudices underlying the increasingly dominant Anglo-Protestant culture prevailing among both settlers and winter visitors.

Of course, those census numbers also represent a large number of African-Americans, primarily slaves. The 87,445 people in 1850, for example, included about 39,000 slaves and another 1,000 free blacks. Despite representing such a large percentage of the total population, African Americans appear only at the edges of Condit's novel. While slaves must have been constantly present in George's new world, they make only infrequent appearances, helping passengers off the steamships in Savannah or rowing Captain Ambler's boat back from a logging camp to Welaka. The doctor's man, Jannary, helps with the young New Yorker's first deer hunt, while the black stage drivers from Picolata play melodies on their trumpets as they enter St. Augustine and small black children dance to their tunes in the streets.

The story of Old Tom offers a chance for the author or George, with their Yankee backgrounds, to comment on slavery as an institution. But neither does. While hunting deer, George comes across a camp and suspects it belongs to Old Tom, one of a group of runaway slaves. All the others had returned to their master, who did not regard the sole remaining escapee worth the effort of finding. Even Tom's desire for freedom comes into question when George realizes that he never really tried to get far away, staying close to his master's home. In describing this brief scene, the author never has the highly adaptive George show any concern about either slavery or Tom. Both author and protagonist appear to accept it as part of Florida's cultural environment.

Just as they were invisible in the census, the Seminoles and Miccosukee never appear as people in *A Trip to Florida for Health and Sport*. After the Second Seminole War (1835-1842), the United States' longest, most expensive, and deadliest Indian War, those Seminoles and Miccosukee who had not been relocated recognized that their best course of action was to become invisible, to avoid contact with whites as much as possible, with many slipping away into reservations and swamp land in the southern part of the state, environments most whites avoided.

In the novel Indians exist solely as legends. Captain Stebbins tells George and his friend David stories about "the late Indian war," which the novel also calls the Florida War, when he shows them his "relics" from the conflict. Later, in St Augustine George and his uncle hear the story of the daring escape of Caoccochee (Wild Cat) and Talmus Hadjo from St. Mark's Fort. While he is fascinated by the legends, George also has an adolescent respect for Native American skill when he suspects that he is "not Indian enough" to hunt turkey successfully (86).

Only one scene in the novel, curiously a comic one, suggests some of the new tensions emerging between Seminoles and settlers while the novel was being written. After George and Mr. Hunter fire a rifle repeatedly in a frustrating attempt to kill a fox squirrel, the older man laughs that the shots probably terrified his neighbor Mr. Bliss into believing that the Seminole chief Sam Jones (Abiaka) had returned. In fact, pressure to relocate the remaining Seminoles and open their land to settlers increased during the 1850s. The U.S. Secretary of War, Jefferson Davis, responded by announcing a trade embargo with the Seminoles, sending Army engineers and surveyors into their reservations, and having troops burn their crops. Responding to this increased military encroachment on his people's land, Chief Billy Bowlegs attacked an Army camp in December 1855 and the Third Seminole War (1855-58) began.

Because the manuscript appears to be a first draft, with many of the grammatical and stylistic challenges of early drafts, we have edited it to correct some of the grammar and punctuation, tighten its occasionally rambling prose, and eliminate distracting repetition and inconsistencies. At the same time, we have preserved the work's essential substance, style, tone, and structure. All of the notes within the text are the author's. Our "Afterword" offers a fuller description of the original manuscript, discussions of the book's literary context and characterization, and our editing principles. All the works cited in the introduction appear in the "Works Cited" at the end of the Afterword.

A Note on Place Names

Because natural landmarks tend to change names fairly often, we can only guess at some of those Cyrus Condit mentions (e.g., Yellow Bluff and Orange Point). A few, of course, like Rocky Point and Dunn's Lake, remain. Of the cities and towns which George Morton visits, only Mellonville has disappeared. Originally named after Fort Mellon on Lake Monroe, it was eventually absorbed in 1883 into Sanford, the town Henry Shelton Sanford incorporated just to its west in 1877. (Fort Mellon itself was first known as Fort Monroe, but renamed in honor of Captain Charles Mellon, the only casualty of an attack on the fort in 1837 during the Second Seminole War.)

A few place names in the novel may seem odd to modern readers. The Silver Springs on Lake George which George only reaches on his second attempt, for example, is actually Silver Glen Springs, not the better known Silver Springs near Ocala. The novel also uses the older spelling of Pilatka. During the British occupation of Florida from 1763 to 1783, Denys Rolle attempted to create a Utopian society along the St. Johns. Visionary but autocratic, Rolle planned to use his 80,000 acre plantation in the area that is now East Palatka to rehabilitate the dregs of London life: thieves, pickpockets, beggars, vagabonds, and reformed prostitutes. By the time the Spanish returned in 1783, the experiment that he named Charlotia in honor of George III's queen, but most people called Rollestown or Rollston, had failed and was abandoned.

When the United States acquired Florida, the deep waters of the area attracted shipping and settlers, who named their community Pilatka, using an anglicized form of the area's original Seminole name (*pilotaikita*, meaning crossing). George Morton and Cyrus Condit would have known it by that name in the 1850s, when it was a popular winter haven for ailing Northerners. In 1875 the post office changed the spelling to Palatka to distinguish it more clearly from Picolata.

During the 1850s, Florida's cities and towns reflected the area's history with a combination of European, American, Creek and Seminole names. The oldest, Saint Augustine, for example, was named in honor of St. Augustine of Hippo, on whose feast day, August 28, 1565, Pedro Menéndez first saw the land on which he would create North America's oldest city. Jacksonville, of course, was re-named from its original Cowford for General Andrew Jackson, the territory's first American military governor and the man whose raids and belligerence were primarily responsible for encouraging the Spanish to sell Florida to the United States.

Enterprise is a testament to the enterprising spirit of a score of industrious settlers, led by Cornelius Taylor, the first cousin of Gen. Zachary Taylor, who founded it in 1841 on the site of the abandoned Fort Kingsbury, which had been built during the Florida War across Lake Monroe from Fort Mellon. The large hotel the author describes in Enterprise is certainly Brock House, built by the crusty, entrepreneurial steamship captain Jacob Brock in 1854 and capable of holding over 50 guests. In 1927 the owner of the Benson Springs Hotel managed to have the town renamed Benson Springs, but by 1937 the town was once again Enterprise.

The St. Johns River itself is simply a translation of its Spanish name, Rio de San Juan, which the Spanish had adopted from the Catholic mission of San Juan del Puerto on Fort George Island near the river's mouth. Much earlier, the Spanish had called it Rio de Corrientes—the River of Currents—and the French Rivière du Mai for the month they first saw it. The Ocklawaha River, on the other hand, appears to have gained its name from the Seminole/Creek word for muddy, *aklowahe*. And Welaka, the small settlement where much of the story occurs, is an English form of the Seminole's original name for the St. Johns, *ylacco* or river of lakes. (In Chapter II Condit comments that the St. Johns passes through so many lakes that it can be considered a chain of lakes as much as a river.)

While Tocoi appears to be the Timucuan word for water lily, there are claims of both Spanish and Native American origins for Picolata, where the naturalist William Bartram had an indigo plantation in 1766. The word could stem from a combination of the Spanish *pico* and *lato* to describe its broad bluff, or it could come from either the Creek word *opiki* (twisted) or the Seminole word *holohata* (blue).

Every project like this requires enormous support and encouragement. We deeply appreciate the patience and good humor of our families, friends and colleagues. And we especially want to thank those who provided significant help to the project: the remarkably talented Michelle Webb for her cover photograph; Dr. Ben Brotemarkle and his staff at the Florida Historical Society for their unflagging commitment to our state's heritage; Laurie Joyner, Dean of the Faculty at Rollins, for her understanding of the essential relationship between teaching and scholarship; Jonathan Miller, Director of the Olin Library, and all his superb librarians and staff; Trudy Laframboise, the Olin Library's inimitable archival specialist; Karen Slater, the English Department's Administrative Assistant, who always finds a way to solve even the most knotty problems; Johnny Smith of Welaka; J. Charlotte Jarrett for editorial suggestions; and the late A.J. Hanna, the Rollins Professor of History and Vice President who helped establish the Florida Collection. We also thank the Rollins students who assisted us: Robert Clark, Jason Gordon, and Timothy Maurer. The Critchfield Fund and the Curry Chair Endowment provided financial support for the project. Some of the discussion of Chateaubriand, Robert Montgomery Bird and the Rev. Michael Smith first appeared in essays originally published in the 2006 and 2007 editions of *Florida Studies*, edited by Claudia Slate, Steve Glassman, and Keith Huneycutt.

Maurice O'Sullivan
Kenneth Curry Professor of Literature
Rollins College

Wenxian Zhang
Professor of Library Science
and Head of Archives and
Special Collections
Rollins College

CHAPTER I

GEORGE MORTON — PREPARES FOR A TRIP TO FLORIDA — THE VESSEL SAILS — SEA SICKNESS — A STEAMER ASHORE — RESCUE OF PASSENGERS — GULF STREAM — A STORM — ARRIVAL AT SAVANNAH — A WALK IN SAVANNAH

George Morton, the hero of our story, was a lad of seventeen years of age. His parents had always resided in the great City of New York, but George had been boarding at a school in the country for several years. After his father died of consumption about a year before the commencement of our tale, his mother, feeling lonely as she had but one other child, decided that George should live at home. Attending school in the city, George, a tall, slender lad, became very interested in his studies and applied himself closely to them. In the spring, he caught a bad cold and developed a cough which lasted all summer and into the fall. Alarmed about his health, his mother consulted her family physician, who advised George to give up his studies for a time, take more exercise in the open air, and winter in the South, especially during the extreme cold weather.

Since his father's death, George's Uncle James, a bachelor who lived with his sister, had become very fond of him. When Uncle James heard the physician's advice, he told them that he had thought of spending the coming winter in Florida himself for his rheumatism and would willingly take George with him.

Despite her reluctance to let him go, Mrs. Morton was willing to do anything that might help him and agreed that Uncle James and George should go to Florida in December. George was delighted with the idea, since he had heard and read of the excellent fishing and hunting there, and at once started preparing. He bought a variety of fishing tackle. While he was living in the country, he had hunted squirrels, birds and rabbits, becoming a very good shot for his age. His father had given him an excellent double barreled shotgun; so he put it in the best of order and bought powder and different kinds of shot, including buckshot for deer. In fact, he dreamt of nothing but hunting deer, and he anticipated more pleasure from that than anything else on his trip.

One stormy December day, George and Uncle James loaded their trunks on a carriage, bid Mrs. Morton and George's brother Willie good bye, promised to write often, and rode downtown to the wharf near the Battery, where the small steamship docked. Uncle James chose it because he knew the owners and had never sailed in a screw steamship. When they arrived, the steamer was taking in some freight and the baggage of its few passengers, so George raced down to his stateroom to stow his carpet bag and get back on deck.

At the appointed hour the crew cast the fastenings off; friends of the passengers bade a final adieu and hurried on shore; the engineer's bell tinkled; the screw began to revolve; and the ship steamed quickly out of her dock, turning her bows toward the Narrows.

And now George was fairly under way. Although it would take only three days and he had often sailed small boats and rowed, he had never before been out of sight of land. Once the vessel began to roll in the heaving waves and the evening cold rose, the passengers all gathered in the main cabin. As they got farther and farther down the lower bay and out to sea, ever larger waves and more rolling drove the passengers, one by one, into their staterooms. Even George soon found that he too was getting sea sick.

Most boys at some time in their lives dream about going to sea. They imagine it all romance and pleasure and think themselves so strong and brave that they will never be sick. But if they do go, they usually find that they have been sadly mistaken. Many a boy who has run away from a good home and tender and loving parents to go to sea has repented of it bitterly and, in most cases, very quickly too. For sea sickness takes all the bravery out of one. It is bad enough to be sick where you have a comfortable stateroom and someone to attend on your wants, but to be sick and abused—kicked about, laughed at and ordered to get up and go to work—that is what boys who run away and go to sea generally get. Think of midnight hours on dark stormy nights, wet and cold, with no place but a wet bunk to lie down in when your work is done. But a sailor's work is never done. He is liable to be called up at any moment, perhaps to go aloft in the dark to fold sails while the vessel pitches and rolls in a storm. Surely, "A sailor's life is a dog's life." Let no boy who reads this, and who has a good home and kind parents, ever think of running away and going to sea.

Each stateroom contained two berths. George had the upper and Uncle James, who had been at sea a number of times and rarely ever became sea sick, the lower. During the evening his uncle looked in on George a number of times and spoke a cheering word or two. George did not talk much to him, hoping he would get to sleep and forget his troubles. But he could not sleep. And long after Uncle James came in and went to bed, or as the sailors say "turned in," the boy lay awake and listened to the creaking of the rudder, the rattling of the rudder chains as they were drawn back and forth, the tramping of the sailors on deck, and the noisy pounding of the propeller shaft, which thumped each time it revolved. Toward morning George fell into a sound sleep and did not awake until the noise of men washing down the decks over his head awoke him.

He did not feel very well but he dressed and went on deck, where he found his uncle. It was a beautiful calm morning. He found the fore sail and fore top sail set, and the ship moved steadily through the water. His uncle told him that, at just about daybreak, they "spoke a vessel" which informed them that a "screw steamer was on shore about thirty miles north of Cape Hatteras." Captain Postley had decided at once to go there, especially as there might be passengers who needed help.

During the morning a side wheel steamer passed them bound in the opposite direction. George asked his uncle why they had not come in a side wheel ship instead of a propeller and which was better.

"I will tell you," said Uncle James. "I have sailed in side wheel steamers often but never in a propeller. And as they are coming into use so much, I wished to sail in one and judge for myself the comparative merits of each method of propulsion."

"I do not exactly understand how a propeller works," said George. "They call them screw steamships; it is not a screw that makes us go, is it?"

"You have seen sailors scull a boat, have you not?"

"Yes," said George. "I can scull a boat myself."

"Well, a propeller works on the same principle. The blades of the propeller are like the section of a screw and are set at such an angle that, as they revolve, they push the water away from them, which forces the vessel ahead."

"But are not the side wheel ships much faster?"

"They have always been so, but lately such improvements have been made in propellers that some are almost as fast as side wheel ships. The great difference in favor of screw steamers is that they can run at half the cost. Since the screw under the stern of the vessel is always submerged, those steamers can carry a sail with a side wind which a side wheel cannot because one wheel would be too deeply submerged and the other one too much out of water. With a strong side wind, propellers often outsail side wheel steamers."

This day passed pleasantly for George. Captain Postley invited his uncle and him into the pilot house, where they were out of the wind and could see about on three sides through the windows. During the day George used Uncle James' opera glass to examine passing vessels and watch the porpoises that swam alongside the ship. They seemed to take a delight in doing so and frequently there would be as many as ten at once close to the vessel and just under the surface of the water. Occasionally they would put their noses out of the water and give a snort as they dashed along without seeming to make any effort to keep up with the ship.

George slept well that night. There was just enough motion to the vessel, which ran only at half speed, to rock him to sleep. When he went on deck the next morning, he found the officers examining the shore through a telescope. They had discovered the grounded vessel and were moving cautiously towards it, although they were still ten miles from the land. After a time the steamer came to anchor, still a long distance from the land.

The neighborhood of Cape Hatteras is a dangerous one for vessels to be caught near in a storm. Uncle James showed George the line of beakers which extended halfway around the horizon. To the south, Cape Hatteras stretched out; and through the glass the land appeared covered with low stunted pine trees. Opposite them, the beached vessel could be seen with the naked eye. Even with a glass the ship did not appear injured. They could see people walking on the beach around her and unloading goods from her bows, which at low tide were high and dug out of water.

At 8 a.m. Captain Postley and two of the crew put off for the wreck in a life boat. George watched them until they became a mere black speck in the distance. After several hours they returned, unable to find any place where the beakers would allow them to land. The other ship had struck on a bar, beaten over it into deep water and then gone on the shore. On this outer bar, the breakers were very high and the water six feet deep. If a boat were to get swamped, its crew would be in deep water and still have several hundred yards to go to reach the shore. At noon the captain put off again and, at the same time, George could see a boat from the shore trying to get through the surf. After several trials, it succeeded and the two boats met each other.

Presently the captain came back. He had seen the captain of the vessel, who told him that they had been grounded nearly a week, that the passengers were all well and no one had been injured, and that with assistance he hoped to free his vessel. Since his crew was not willing to leave their boat, he had to hire North Carolina wreckers, who brought him off in one of their boats. Captain Postley had promised to remain until the surf went down enough to allow the wreckers to take the stranded passengers off, unless a storm set in. George spent the rest of the day talking with the officers and the other passengers, while white sea gulls flew about the ship in great numbers, occasionally alighting on the water in little groups.

The next morning, Sunday, was lovely. Going on deck, George saw another steamer coming toward them. It anchored close by and the captain came on board to learn from Captain Postley how matters stood. At about 10 a.m. two boats, loaded with baggage, came from shore manned by the wreckers, a rough looking party of men. As they lay alongside, the sailors bandied jokes with them.

Shortly after, two boats from each steamer and the two wreckers' boats put off for the shore to try to bring back the stranded passengers. It was a pretty sight to see as the six boats pulled off over the long swell that rolled in from the Southeast. George watched with great interest through opera glasses as the wreckers passed the bar and brought all the passengers safely through the surf, transferring them to the boats from the steamers. As the passengers and crew lined the side of their vessel, they watched the boat carrying the ladies with especial interest. When a boat finally came alongside, first an umbrella was handed up, then a bandbox, then a lady and son, until all were out except a lady with two children.

The children, a little boy and girl, appeared delighted with their situation. The captain took one of them in his arm and, with help from his men, climbed up the side of the vessel; then the baby was handed up. One of the sailors tossed up a bonnet but no one caught it and away it went, to be fished out eventually with an umbrella.

There were five ladies and six gentlemen in the party, and they had been ashore nearly a week. Although they had had plenty to eat and drink, at certain states of the tide the stern of the vessel would thump so that they could not sleep. In time they might have gone ashore and made tents, but they were in no immediate danger. They could have crossed Pamplica Sound to the mainland in boats, but they would have had to walk a great way through the sand before they came to a habitable place. As the ladies could not do that, they all decided to remain by the ship and hope for a rescue. They were all in good humor and glad to be once more on the water. As soon as the boats were hoisted in and the anchor weighed, the steamer got under way once more.

Late that afternoon a line of white foam caught George's eye. As far as he could see, it stretched away from one edge of the horizon to the other. He instantly realized that it must be the Gulf Stream and, finding his uncle below, asked him to come up and see if it were. By the time they got on deck, the ship was just passing through the line of foam. On the side they had been sailing on, the water was a dark green. But as soon as they crossed the line, the water became dark blue and seemed more agitated, heaving up in short broken waves. The line between the two waters was as distinct as that between land and sea; and the moment they crossed, the temperature of the air changed as if it blew from some hot shore.

Captain Postley told them that the Gulf Stream was nearer to the coast that winter than he had ever seen it. Before that winter he had never entered it between New York and Savannah. It was ordinarily fifty miles from Cape Hatteras but this winter it was within thirty miles. The line of foam came from the chafing of the moving water against water at rest, a phenomenon George had lately studied in his Physical Geography class.

That night the full moon arose with unclouded beauty, so George and his uncle sat on deck until late enjoying the scene. The waves ran higher than they had been before and the wind blew straight ahead, but the air had become so warm and pleasant that George felt as if he could have remained there all night. It was so delightful to watch the reflection of the moon across the great expanse of waters lighting up the crest of every wave. Some of the ladies began singing a familiar hymn and soon everyone joined in for a number of sweet hymns.

It was a scene well calculated to make all feel their dependence upon Him. This great heaving, tossing waste of waters all rolling and tossing before His winds and obeying His will. What is man and all his proud ships before it when "He commandeth, and raiseth the stormy wind, which lifteth up the waves thereof"? George could not help thinking of these things and he silently lifted up his heart to God as he did night and morning to protect him and all on board and to bring them safely to their journey's end. That night the wind kept increasing and in the morning it blew so hard that the vessel could not make much headway against it. They passed out of the Gulf Stream during the night.

Monday was miserable for George, who was sick all day and could eat nothing. The straight ahead wind caused the vessel to pitch, which was much worse than the rolling motion. During the morning it rained, and poor George had to leave the deck and go into the cabin. Here the air was so warm and close that it made him feel worse than ever. When he returned to the deck, notwithstanding the rain, he met the First Engineer, who invited him into his room, which was in a house on deck. The Engineer told him that he could remain there as long as he wished, so he and Uncle James sat there all day long. Since the cabin was amidships, they felt the pitching of the vessel less than in their cabin and fastened the door open so they had all the fresh air they wished. Uncle James tried to amuse George by telling him about his adventures traveling around the world, but it was hard to interest or amuse poor George. The Steward brought up tea and food, but the boy could neither eat nor drink.

Since the Engineer kindly told them that they could use his room as long as they wished, they decided to remain in it all night. But George did not sleep much. During the night a squall struck, giving the ship a tremendous roll and shifting almost everything in the room. Down came a hatbox containing the Engineer's "go ashore" hat and struck George in the face; and by the clatter in the closet, he realized that a pitcher of water had overturned. The rain driven by the wind struck the house almost as sharply as hail; the wind howled and roared through the rigging; and presently they heard the loud flapping of a sail and the voices of the officers shouting to the men. In the morning, they saw that the foresail had split during the squall and that part of it had had to be cut away. They found the floor of their room all wet from the toppled pitcher of water and everything in confusion.

On Tuesday, the wind moderated and the sea calmed down. George felt better at once. Towards night they made land but, with no pilot on board, were obliged to anchor off the mouth of the Savannah River all night. The next morning all were up and on deck early. Everyone had recovered from their seasickness and smiled at the prospect of being on land again in a few hours. Once a pilot arrived, the ship began moving again, passing the lighthouses on Tybee Island, an old ruined fort and, farther up the river, two other forts. The shores were low, mostly large fields lying along the banks of the river.

The color of the river, a little like smoked salmon, at once attracted George's attention. Uncle James said it was the same color as the Mississippi River. As they came near the city of Savannah, the river's channel, crooked and in places quite narrow, seemed too narrow for the number of large ships and steamships lying at the wharves. When the steamer drew up to its wharf, a large gang of negroes got a platform up to help passengers go ashore. Once George and his uncle landed, they went by omnibus to a hotel.

As there yet remained several hours before dinner, they sallied out to look at the city. They expected to leave for Florida the next morning and, therefore, had to see what they wished of Savannah that afternoon. Near the hotel in a square stood a white monument which Uncle James told George was formerly called the Greene and Polaski monument in honor of the Revolutionary War's Generals Greene and Polaski, who commanded the unsuccessful attack of the Americans on Savannah while it was occupied by the British. In the attack Gen. Polaski fell mortally wounded. They were told that a new monument had been erected to Polaski, and they walked out though one of the principal streets to see it.

"Did you ever see a place with so many squares and such handsome trees in them?" asked George.

"There are a great many," replied Uncle James. "I think the plan of this city is the best of any city I know."

"See," said George, "how green and beautiful the trees are. What kind are these?"

"They are mostly Water Oaks, which retain their leaves all winter until the new leaves push them off in the spring."

"How pleasant it is to be here in the middle of winter walking under the green trees, especially when we contrast it with the snow and ice and the bare hills and trees at home," said George.

"Do you think that you would rather live where there was no snow and ice?"

"Oh, I don't know about that," replied George. "I like to skate and to sleigh ride, and have always enjoyed the winters very much. Perhaps, though, I should like the South better. But then I have been here but a few hours and do not know enough about it to make any comparisons."

"I am glad to hear you come to so good a conclusion. Many people who travel can see nothing good in anything that differs from what they have become accustomed to. They jump at conclusions, go grumbling about, and seem determined not to be pleased with anything."

They presently came to the square with the new Polaski Monument. After admiring it, they visited the park and the enormous freight depots of the Georgia Bemthal Rail Road, where they saw thousands of bales of cotton. The streets leading from the depots were filled with carts and drags carting the cotton to the ships at the wharves.

After dinner they took a drive in a carriage to a grove of live oak treescalled Bonaventure. It was a beautiful sight, aisles of great live oaks with long gray moss hanging in festoons and swaying in the wind. They also saw a part of the grove used as a cemetery and the oak trees planted so many years ago and visited by all who remain in Savannah long enough. Finally, they drove to Jasper Spring, the place where Sergeant Jasper and Private Newton captured a British guard of ten men and set a party of American prisoners free.

CHAPTER II

LEAVE SAVANNAH — CROSS ST. JOHN'S RIVER BAR —
JACKSONVILLE — UP THE RIVER — WELAKA — WELAKA
SPRING — GAR FISH — DUCK HUNTING BY FIRELIGHT — OR-
ANGE GROVES — FIRST DEER HUNT — WOUNDS A DEER

The next morning they boarded the steamboat St. Johns and soon left the city of Savannah far behind. By looking on a map of Georgia, you will see that the whole east of that state is lined with the islands that produce the famous Sea Island Cotton. When the tide among the numerous rivers and sounds within the islands suits, steamboats can sail from Savannah nearly to the mouth of the St. Johns River without going onto the ocean. Since many of the channels are very narrow and shallow, steamboats using this inside passage often have to remain until the tide rises.

Although the day was pleasant, the tide was not, so the captain took the outside passage. The sea was smooth and the steamboat ran down the coast in sight of the shore, passing through one of the channels at dark. During the night, they touched at Darien, Brunswick and St. Marys. When George arose in the morning, they were just coming up to the wharf at Fernandina, on the western shore of Amelia Island, a new and busy little town. A railroad is being built to connect it with Cedar Key on the Gulf of Mexico.

As the tide would not allow them to continue on the channel inside Amelia Island, they turned back and passed around its northern end. In moving out to sea, they had to cross a bar with great waves. Watching from the rail near the pilot house, George saw several of the largest waves break over the bow of the boat, filling the forward deck with water a foot deep. Within a few hours they saw the lighthouses at the mouth of the St. Johns River. But as they drew nearer to shore, he saw the great beakers on the bar, one of the worst on the whole coast. A bit of the wreck of the steamboat Welaka was still visible on it. They crossed the bar without accident and entered the river where a number of vessels, loaded with lumber, waited for favorable winds and tides to allow them to cross the bar and get to sea.

The St. Johns starts in south Florida and runs north to Jacksonville, where it turns and flows east to the Atlantic. From its mouth up to Pilatka, it varies from half a mile to three or four miles in width. From there to Lake George it is generally a quarter mile wide. Farther South it narrows, often no wider than fifty feet and very crooked. Steamboats regularly run as high as Enterprise, occasionally going thirty or forty miles still farther south. The St. Johns passes through so many lakes that some call it a chain of lakes instead of a river.

George and his uncle had left the trees at home bare and the hills covered with snow, but here the shore looked beautiful, like mid-summer, as they passed it. They intended to remain in Jacksonville, where they left the boat which proceeded on to Pilatka, only a few days so they could go farther south. Here George saw guavas, pomegranates, mangoes, and other tropical fruit growing in a garden. Uncle James became acquainted with a gentleman who resided at Welaka and invited them to visit him there. As they planned to go farther up the river, he decided to do so, and made up a little party of some pleasant persons who were traveling for health, to go in the next boat.

One beautiful morning they boarded the Steamboat Barnett[1] and were soon steaming up the river. They reached Pilatka that afternoon and, remaining there all night, sailed at daybreak again to reach Welaka in about two hours. On the way up the river, they saw a great many wild ducks, and different kinds of herons and cranes. There were great numbers of white cranes about three feet high, and some of the passengers amused themselves by shouting at them. But the noise of the steamboat frightened them so that they could not get near enough for successful shouting. In the summer time a great many alligators pass up or down the river, but in cold weather they rarely come out of the water. The passengers constantly talked about the luxuriant vegetation along the river banks. Where the shores were swampy, osprey and gum trees predominated. But where they were higher, pines and the oaks were the principal growth.

---

1   Since then blown up, near Jacksonville.

Welaka is one of the most beautiful places on the St. Johns. It consists of about a dozen houses built on a high shell bank[2] on the eastern shore; behind them the soil is sandy and covered with pine woods. The boarding house, situated right on the river bank, had a flight of steps that led down to a platform where a number of small boats were kept.

That morning they walked out to look at the saw mill and the country around Welaka. In the afternoon they went to see the Welaka Spring. After a pleasant walk of three quarters of a mile, they came to the spring at the head of a cove running up from the river. The residents have built a bath house over it. Since the temperature of the water was 71 degrees in summer and winter and as the day was warm, George had the pleasure of taking a bath in the open air in the month of January. The water is very clear, but strongly impregnated with sulfur. The bottom slats of the bathing house and logs lying near are covered with sulphurous deposits. The boil of water at the heart of the spring was about ten feet square, and the quantity of water flowing from it would have been enough to power a mill. Overhanging the cove were great trees, the resort of numerous herons and cranes. The cove itself abounded with gar fish, a voracious species that are not fit for food but prey upon smaller fish and continually break the surface of the water in their attacks. Some of the gar are upwards of four feet long with large, thick scales and heads that terminate in a long bill armed with large sharp teeth.

George now spent a week hunting ducks. Though there were great numbers of them, they were very shy. They had been hunted all the way down the coast from the shores of Delaware Bay. Having gotten used to the sight of a boat and the sound of a gun, they took the alarm quickly. He had no other way to hunt them except by rowing directly towards them and shooting as they tried to fly. Although he wounded a great many, they would most always be able to fly away or to dive and keep out of sight. Still, he enjoyed rowing; and as there were several young men at the boarding house, he never lacked company.

The Ocklawaha is a long, narrow, deep and crooked river that passes through some of the richest counties in Florida and empties into the St. Johns nearly opposite Welaka. A number of barges ply between the different landings on it and Pilatka, some propelled by steam and others poled along by the boatmen. George took great pleasure in rowing on the Ocklawaha. It was generally not more than forty feet wide, although very deep. For several miles up from its mouth it flows

---

2   There are many of these "shell banks" along the River. They are composed of myriads of small fresh water shells mingled with the earth.

through a swamp and is overhung by cypress, gum and other swamp trees, which gives it a peculiarly wild and melancholy appearance. He would sometimes row up for a mile or so and then float down with the current. In this way, on turning a bend in the river, he would sometimes come suddenly on a flock of ducks.

One afternoon an immense number of ducks passed up the river. As it was near dark, he was pretty certain that they would go no farther than Little Lake George, about a mile south of Welaka. One person mentioned that he had seen ducks hunted by firelight at night. Since this was something novel, a little party was made up to try it that night. Captain Stebbins, Mr. Brown, David and George met at the wharf in the captain's boat a little after dark, each with a double barreled gun. The captain and Mr. Brown got the lightwood ready, while David and George put the boat in order. Lightwood, the best material for making a quick bright fire, can be had wherever pitch or yellow pine trees grow. When a pine tree dies from any cause that leaves it standing, the bark and sap rot off and leave the heart, which is much harder and does not rot but will stand for a great number of years. As it gets seasoned, full of resinous substances, it burns with a brighter, hotter flame than any other kind of wood.

After cutting some lightwood into small pieces and passing them into the boat, they prepared two boxes. The first would lie in the bottom of the boat and support the second, which would be filled with sand so a fire could be built on it. They got under way at 10 p.m. and rowed quietly up to the point which forms the northern boundary of the lake. Stopping to fill their box with sand, they shoved off to pass around the point into the lake. The night was darker than they wished, with clouds hiding a large part of the stars, but they could easily distinguish the nearest shore of the lake, about five miles broad at its widest part. The captain and George sat in the bow with their guns heavily loaded, and the other two rowed. A little way into the lake, a match was applied to the pile of wood and in a few minutes a broad light shone over the water about them.

They were just getting underway nicely, when one of them made a sudden movement which tipped the boat. In an instant the box and all the fire fell over into the water, and they found themselves in what seemed total darkness. Furious were the exclamations of surprise and vexation, but they finally ended in a hearty laugh. What was to be done now? The box full of sand has sunk. It seemed at first as if they must give up their expedition. But they decided to turn the remaining box on end, cover it with mud and try the fire on it. So they rowed back to the point and landed among the trees. Then they lighted a pine knot and by its light, plastered one end of the box with mud, making a wall around the edges. They thought this would do as well as the first arrangement, except that it was not as high as they would have liked.

Again they got under way and lighted their fire. As they rowed slowly up the eastern shore of the lake, George watched the water intently where the farthest line of light fell on it, hoping to see a flock of ducks. But none appeared. After an hour searching the eastern shore, they crossed the lake and moved slowly down the western shore. Changing places with David, George took the stern paddle. They had returned to within a mile of their starting place and were talking about throwing the fire overboard and pulling for home, when they heard a loud roaring sound on all sides. Bang-bang. Bang-bang went the guns in the bow; and the captain shouted, "Pull to the right. I shot some there."

"Pull to the left," shouted David. "I shot some too."

The noise of the ducks, the smoke from the fire, and the blindness occasioned by those in the stern looking at the bright fire made it almost impossible for them to tell which way to turn. They picked up only three or four of the birds and then rowed a little farther on. So many ducks rose out of the water that they sounded like thunder. Again, both barrels of both guns fired into the thickest of the flock, but again the hunters found and retrieved only three or four. And now the ducks began smashing into the boat.

The fire seemed to dazzle the birds' eyes so they would fly with great force against the side of the boat and drop into the water. George laid down his paddle and began clutching at those that fell. He caught several, but most sunk the instant they struck the water. The captain stepped on one which had flown into the box and dropped into the boat. Soon after, a foot long mullet jumped out of the water and would have landed in the boat, had he not met the captain's face, ripping off a piece of skin and falling overboard. Finally, all the ducks seemed to have crossed to the eastern side of the lake; and the party decided to turn homewards since it was very late. When the excitement was over, they realized that if they had only put down their guns and picked up sticks of wood, they might have knocked down great numbers of ducks. The next night they went again, taking only a little fire in a long handled pan. With this they did better, although they did not get amongst such a large flock.

George had had his imagination excited in regard to Florida oranges. He had expected to find them in great abundance, but, like most people who go to Florida, he was disappointed. Several severe frosts a number of years ago killed all the old trees; and, more recently, an insect has ravaged the sweet (i.e., cultivated) orange trees and fruit. But there are two other distinct kinds of oranges in Florida which grow wild. Large natural groves of sour oranges grow throughout the state. Despite their intensely sour taste, some people like and eat them. They are also very good in making orangeade, and some people make a preserve of them. The other kind is called "bitter sweets." Their peel is very thick and the skin between and around the sections intensely bitter. But the pulp and juice are sweet and pleasant. At first taste, most people dislike them. But once the visitor learns how to open them correctly and get at the sweet without tasting the bitter, they are excellent.

On the point a mile above Welaka was a small grove of wild oranges, so George and a party, including Uncle James, walked there one day. Although the grove looked beautiful with ripe tempting fruit hanging in bunches of three to six and eight, the majority of the trees were of the sour kind. The only way they could distinguish between them was to taste the fruit from each tree. George tried this but soon found that his teeth set on edge by the fruit's sourness. The very few bitter sweet trees in the grove were not marked by the distinctive cross cut in the bark as they are in more visited groves.

Wild oranges are more reddish than sweet ones. At last the party found one tree of excellent bitter sweets and, sitting on a fallen oak, ate all they wished. The trees are bushy and very thorny, and it is difficult to climb into them without tearing one's clothes or hands. Since the oranges are not easily knocked off, some lazy people cut the trees down to get the fruit. The best way to get it involves using a long forked stick to twist the fruit off. Each member of the party furnished himself with an orange wood cane from the sprouts shooting up out of the roots of the trees.

Because they had visited a wild orange grove, they now wished to visit a sweet orange grove. Since there are several on Anzie (or Drayton) Island, at the entrance to Lake George about twelve miles south of Welaka, they got a good sailboat and kept it ready for the first fair wind. The wind soon came, and one beautiful morning a party of six set out. George rowed them up to the point; there the wind was fair, and they hoisted sail and went bounding across Little Lake George and through the narrow part of the river beyond it. From there the river was a mile wide, and in places wider; and the wind still being fair, they were at the boat landing on the island by noon.

Anzie Island contains about two thousand acres of land, mostly covered with pine forest. A gentleman from Georgia had lately purchased it, with the intention of spending his winters there. He received them kindly and invited them to walk out into the grove nearest the house. Here were two-handed trees of fifteen to twenty years growth. Many of the trees were as large around as a man's head, generally growing in clumps of three or four. With a forked stick they twisted off as many as they could eat and then filled their pockets and a bag. Every member of the expedition pronounced them the finest oranges they had ever tasted. The difference between a ripe orange picked from the tree and eaten at once and one that has been picked green and shipped a long distance is astonishing.

They also saw a number of curious plants on the island, among them a century plant that had bloomed the preceding summer. After many thanks to the gentlemanly proprietor, they sailed for home. On the way they shot some ducks, but the wind dying early in the afternoon obliged them to row home, arriving at dark. They were all highly delighted with their trip.

The only regular religious services in Welaka, were those held once a month by a traveling Methodist minister, who preached in one of the village's empty houses. On the other Sundays, some of the boarders in the house would generally read a sermon. Those who were Episcopalians would read a part of the Church Service and then all would join in singing hymns. They invited their neighbors, who sometimes filled the parlor. The villagers believed that even this humble service was far better than making no attempt to worship God.

The western shore of the St. Johns River, from Pilatka up to Lake George is mostly swampy. Although the swamps had deer in considerable numbers, trees and undergrowth were so thick that it was almost impossible to get a shot at them. A log causeway built across the swamp, opposite Welaka, had become so decayed as to be seldom used. Where the causeway joined the hammock, the woods were more open. There hunters put their dogs out to run the deer past the hammock, where they could get a shot at them. The local doctor, who was very fond of hunting and kept some hounds, invited Uncle James, George and several others to go over with him to the hammock and try for a deer. The chances were not very favorable but a party was made up. But we will let George tell the story of his first deer hunt himself in a letter to his mother, which we will give entire.

Welaka Fla. Jan 10th 185-

My Dear Mother

My cough is still improving and I am more and more delighted with the climate of Fla. every day. I am now going to give you a description of my first and second deer hunts. You know how much I have talked about hunting deer. So this letter will all be about it.

The hunt was made up of Uncle James, Mr. Brown, David, the Dr. and his man Jannary, and myself. We heard the Dr.s' horn just after breakfast and went down to the wharf. You had ought to have seen how comically Uncle James looked with his pantaloons tucked into his boots, and a hunting cap with an enormous front to it (which he borrowed) on. The Dr. soon came to the wharf with his man, and four hounds. We all got in a boat, and Jannary rowed us over the landing at the end of the causeway. The causeway had been made of logs cut and lain crosswise in the swamp, and when first built might have been a tolerably good road for a swamp road, but many of the logs had been decayed and a person had to be careful where they stepped or they would go through into the mud, or injure themselves. The trees grew thickly on either side, and the way was so partly overgrown with bushes and briars so that we were all thankful when we reached the end of it and once more stood on solid earth. The hammocks are lands elevated several feet above the swamps, and are the richest lands in Fla. They are generally thickly covered with live oaks, cabbage, pal-mettoe[3], and other kinds of trees. From the end of the causeway the road or path continued on through the hammock.

The Dr. placed us at different "stands", along the path at about a hundred yards apart. The trees were so thick that we could not see each other, but we were not about to fire up or down the path on any consideration. The Dr. expected to "jump" a deer very quickly, and said that he would most likely, cross the road, at some one of the places where he had posted us. He and Jannary then took the dogs and started off to put them in the swamp. They had been gone but a little time, when I heard the dogs "open" as if on a trail, and soon after they commenced yelling furiously, as if they had jumped a deer, but instead of

3   Called by some "Palmettoe trees"- by others "cabbage trees."

coming towards us, they went in an opposite direction. Then we heard the Dr.s' horn, and he blew for the dogs a long time, but the dogs did not hear it, or at any rate, they did not heed it, for they kept on in the chase, their cries growing fainter and fainter until lost in the distance. After a time the Dr. came to us and said that, they had jumped a deer and ran him off, but he would probably come back again. So we all got together and ate our lunch, listening meanwhile, so as to run back to our stands in case we heard the dogs coming. But we waited in vain, until late in the afternoon, only hearing them occasionally, at a great distance. The Dr. kept blowing his horn and said that he should wait until dark, for he thought that the deer would come that way again.

Finally the Dr. and David started toward where the dogs were last heard, Jannary sat down under a tree, and the rest of us, concluded to try, and get over the causeway, while it was light enough to do so, without danger of breaking our legs. We arrived at the landing without further incident, except a few falls; we followed to the people opposite on the wharf, who sent a boat over for us. We found that they had delayed dinner for the party to return, and that the ladies at the house had made a crown, with which to crown the man who killed the deer. But no one was crowned of course. At eight o'clock we heard the Dr.s' horn, and went to see if he had had any luck. He had no deer but said that if we had remained at our stands we could have had one, as Jannary said that shortly after we left a deer ran up close to where he was and stood still, listening to the dogs. He had no gun and so could not shoot it.

I was somewhat disappointed with the ill luck of my first hunt, but still it did not dampen my valor at all, as I cannot expect success every time. So when the next day the Dr. asked me if I should like to go again I told him "yes, I was ready for it, at any time." He said "he thought of going that afternoon, for as the deer were there, we should stand a chance to get one." We had an early dinner, and then set out; Jannary only accompanying us. When we reached the hammock, he put me at a stand near where I had formerly been placed. I stood behind a large tree on the edge on an opening in the woods. In front of me was shallow pond, which was full of long grass. The Dr. told me that he had shot several deer there, and that they generally ran close to the tree, beside which I took my post.

He then went on and put the dogs in, and in a few minutes they opened so fiercely, that I knew they had jumped a deer. They were coming from the direction where the Dr. was, and I kept expecting to hear his gun every moment, but did not. They kept coming closer and closer to me, and I was listening eagerly and looking sharply, when I heard a little noise at the edge of the grass pond and saw a pair of horns, coming through the grass. The deer was wading slowly through the water, where the grass was so high that I could not see his body. I cocked my gun the instant I saw the horns, but as he was coming partly toward me, I thought I should get a fair shot at him. But he turned suddenly from me. I think he scented me—and I saw that he would be in some thick bushes in an instant; so I raised my gun, and aimed at where I thought his body ought to be, and fired. His horns were gone like a flash, and I thought that perhaps I had shot him, and he had fallen in the long grass. But the dogs came wallowing through the water, and went on yelling their best, so I knew I had not.

The Dr. came up and I told him what had occurred. He laughed and said that "I had done better than he expected, as most beginners forget to fire at the first deer they see." He told me that he had been at a stand, and that the deer was coming down the path directly toward him, when his youngest dog, who had got off the track and returned to him, hearing the other dogs, sprang off toward the deer and turned him, making him lose his shot. We listened to the dogs as they kept on toward the river, and finally they suddenly ceased yelling, and after a short time came back wet. The Dr. said, without a doubt I had wounded the deer and he had taken to the river. A wounded deer will always get into the water if they can. I think I took the affair pretty coolly; if I had fired when I first saw him I would have stood a better chance, as he was going slowly and was nearer to me than when I did fire.

The dogs started another deer and he ran near us twice; but there were trees and bushes between us, so that neither of us saw him. We had excitement enough though to pay us for all our trouble. We did not get back home again until after dark. This is the end of my deer hunting for the present, but I am determined to keep on, for I like the excitement of it, and I shall kill a deer by and by.

The woods are perfumed with the jessamines that are now in blossom, and the trees are putting out their new green leaves. They say here, that spring has commenced. Some of the days are quite warm. I see by the papers that you have had a "cold spell" in N. York. "The cold day" there was cold here too. The thermometer showed 29 degrees in the morning, which is something very unusual for this place.

There is a schooner now here loading with lumber which makes it look a little business like. But it is late at night and I must close up my letter. I have just been to the window and looked out. The moon shines brightly on the river and as there is no air stirring, it looks like glass. The crickets chirp and over in the swamp the owls are hooting, Hoo, Hoo – Hoo, Hoo – Hoo, Hoo. ah. There are no other sounds that I can hear. Give my love to all Dear Mother. I will write soon again. Read this letter all through to Willie.

Your Affectionate Son

George

CHAPTER III

TROLLING FOR TROUT — HUNTING PARTY SET OUT — MR. HUNTER — HIS FAMILY AND CLAIM — ADVICE TO YOUNG HUNTERS — PREPARATIONS FOR THE HUNT — STORY OF A FIGHT WITH A BUCK

It was now near the time for trout fishing on the St. Johns. Several had been caught recently, but no large numbers. The St. Johns trout have nothing in common with Northern brook trout or lake trout, except that they are all fish. Although their general appearance and fins are entirely unlike any of the other members of the trout family, since that is the name they go by on the river, we shall call them trout. These one to ten pound fish are caught in various ways: with a hook, line and line minnows for bait; with a bob (a bunch of red and white rags tied over three hooks and dangled on the water, with a short line and a long springy pole); and by trolling. When they appear in great numbers, they will strike at a bob, by far the easiest way to catch them. But the trolling line is generally used.

For the benefit of any boy who may not know what a troll is, we will state that they are made in various ways. Some of them consist of the bowl of a spoon, made to revolve easily around a wire at the bottom of which three hooks are placed back to back. As the motion of the boat makes the spoon revolve around the wire, one side of the bob seems bright and glittering, like a small fish darting through the water. Although there are various patterns of trolls, or spinners, all are made to revolve by the motion of the boat and thus imitate the movements of a small fish. Deceived by the spinners, the trout dart at them and seize them. Then the boat's motion hooks them, so all you have to do is haul them in very quickly.

One morning George and David got a boat and lines and put off to try their luck trolling. They rowed across the river to the end of a long bend and followed the shore as closely as they dared. While the fish can generally be caught close to the shore, where the little ones go to escape larger trout, there is a danger of catching your hooks on logs or brush fallen in the river if you go too near. David rowed the light boat, and George sat in the stern to fish. He let out about eighty feet of line and kept a number of coils ready to run out in case the hooks got foul of a snag. They were going along pleasantly, when George whirled around, exclaiming, "O! I have got—no *stop the boat*. It is a snag." He let the line run out quickly until David stopped the boat. As he began backing, George drew in the line until they were over the hooks. Looking down, they could see their spinner caught fast to a snag, but by the help of an oar they soon loosed it without injury.

They started again, and in a few minutes George cried out, "Now I have got one."

"Pull him in as fast as you can," said David.

George pulled rapidly on the long line. His fish would break out of the water in its struggles to get free, but he was fairly hooked. As George drew him in over the side of the boat, he shouted, "Hurrah for the first fish! How much does he weigh, David?"

"Oh! That is a middling sized one, about three pounds."

"Why, I should have thought he weighed twice that," said George. "At any rate, it is the largest fish I ever caught."

"If you stay here long, you won't think much of that," said David. "Well, are you ready to try for a six pounder?"

"All ready. Go ahead!"

In a few minutes George had another, and in the course of ten minutes he had caught five. The last one weighed about five pounds.

"Now, David, let me row. You must be tired. It seems selfish for me to do all the fishing," said George.

"Oh! It is nothing new for me; I would rather see you catch them than do it myself. You go at it so earnestly. Besides, I know where most of the snags are and can avoid them." But George insisted and David took the line, but did not catch anything, for the fish seemed to have stopped biting.

So they crossed to the opposite shore, and George took the line. He just got his line out when he sprang up and shouted, "Oh! I've got a rouser—no! It must be caught to a log—stop the boat—no!—It is a fish and a large one too, I tell you." And George kept dangling in his line. At last he hauled a pickerel two feet long into the boat.

"That's what we call a jack fish," said David.

"We call them pickerel in the north," said George. "They are real game fish."

"How did he pull?"

"I was sure once that I was fast to the end of a springy limb. Now you try again, David."

David took the line while George rowed. And in a few minutes David made some quick motions and started handing in his line. "I have a large one this time, too," said he. When he had pulled the fish half way up to the boat, it made a rush and then sprang out of the water and, while in the air, shook itself trying get the hooks out of its mouth. They heard the spinner jingle, but it was securely hooked and David drew it into the boat. The trout was a large one that they thought weighed ten pounds. David caught one more just as he was winding in his line. They pulled home, and George felt very proud of his success as they carried the fish up the steps and into the house. But the people at the house seemed to think it only ordinary luck. This was a little mortifying to him, but he consoled himself with the idea that if better luck was to be had, he stood as good a chance for it as any one. Their fish weighed twenty four and a half pounds all together. The large one that David caught was nine pounds.

There had been some talk of getting up a party to go ten or twelve miles out into the country for a regular hunt near Dunn's Lake, where the game was more plentiful and the woods more open. One morning Mr. Hunter, who resided in that vicinity, was in the village and several of those wishing to go spoke to him. He said he would be glad to have them stay at his house, and he would go on a hunt with them whenever they wished. Since it was a beautiful morning, Mr. Hastings proposed that they go immediately. David and George were willing, but Mr. Hunter had come on horseback and was not prepared to take them and their gear. David's father soon arranged the matter by lending them a cart and harness.

About noon Mr. Hunter mounted the horse that drew the cart. This George found to be the custom all through the south. A man will never sit in his wagon or car to drive if he has a saddle and can sit on his horse. The road was sandy and hilly, and for the first five miles led through a pine barren. It was nothing more than a cart track, which wound through the pine woods and made short turns to avoid fallen trees. The young men rode and walked by turns, passing a great many small lakes and clear ponds with sandy bottoms, generally surrounded by tall coarse grass among which droves of cattle fed. Then they came to better land and passed several log houses and clearings, finally turning from the main track to the one that led directly to Mr. Hunter's. They drove up to his log house through the pine woods an hour or so before dark.

Mr. Hunter, a tall, well formed man with an intelligent countenance, was about forty years of age, although he looked older from the hardships which he had endured. He was born and had lived in North Carolina until he was twenty five, then married and shortly afterward removed to Florida. He never had an opportunity of obtaining much of an education, but his strong good sense and habits of close observation of men and nature made him appear to much better advantage than most of the country people that George became acquainted with in Florida. He had emigrated to one of the richest counties in the state but had had so much sickness in his family that he at last determined to remove to a more healthy part, even if the land was much poorer. He had lately bought and moved to the claim which he now occupied. The house was a common log cabin, containing but two rooms and a shed room. Back from the house, in a separate building, stood the kitchen. Beside this he had a corn house and a building for storing his cotton. There were only thirty acres of land cleared as yet, but he was deadening and fencing more and was preparing to plant cotton, corn and sweet potatoes. He had four children: two grown daughters and two sons, the eldest of whom, James, was a year or so younger than George. The younger, John, was about fourteen.

Mrs. Hunter soon had a dinner ready for them and they did justice to it. They then cleaned their guns and took a short walk until it was dark. Because the night was somewhat chilly, a fire was built in the wide clay fireplace and they sat around enjoying it as only Northern city dwellers who use close stoves and anthracite coal could. They talked principally about hunting, with Mr. Hunter describing the customs near Dunn's Lake. He told them that the deer seldom ever fed out in the open woods during the daytime, as they had been hunted so much lately. Instead, they fed at night and returned to the bays in the daytime.

"What do you mean by the 'bays'?" asked Mr. Hastings.

"Did you not notice, as we were coming here, a number of thick, swampy looking places, full of trees and bushes?" asked Mr. Hunter. "Those places are called 'bay galls' or bays here. There is always a belt of scrub palmetto surrounding them, between them and the big pine land.

"Mr. Pierce, who is best acquainted with the country around here, is coming over with his dogs in the morning and will be driver of the hunt. He will take the dogs and put them in the bays where he thinks there are deer. The rest of us will take stands, where he tells us to, around the bays. If a deer is jumped and there are enough of us to fill all the stands, we are pretty sure of having him."

"Do the deer always run out at the stands?" asked George.

"They most always have their runs and will come out at them unless they are driven away or scent danger. If a deer is not hard pressed by the dogs, he will generally stop just at the edge of the bay to see if the way is clear. A deer trusts more to his nose than his eyes; sometimes they may see you and if you keep perfectly still, will walk toward you as if they wished to find out what you were. But if they once get your scent, they are off. When the dogs are close, they have no time to stop and break out suddenly. Always keep as still as you can after a deer comes out, for if you do not move he will hardly see you. But if you move at all, unless under cover, they will be sure to see you."

"I am very glad to learn these things," said George. "For the fact is I know nothing about hunting deer and I want to get all the information I can."

"All I know is from what I have heard and read," said Mr. Hastings, "and I too would be glad of any advice you can give us."

"Well there is one thing I want to speak to you about. As neither of you knows the country, there may be some danger of your getting lost unless you are careful. I will send you to your stands. Sometimes the deer runs off in a different direction from the one we expect, and then you may see me run to try and get a shot. But you had better keep to your stands. If you find the dogs have all gone off in one direction, you might follow up slowly. Our dogs will not run a deer more than half an hour; that is the way we train them here. We do not want them to be all day after a deer; we want them to come back and start another one. The hunting ground is so surrounded by lakes and ponds that if a deer is run off, he does not come back again that day. But if you get lost, keep your ears open and listen for my horn. There is one other thing—if either of you shoot at a deer and he falls, keep your eye on him. If he attempts to get up, give him the other barrel—don't spare powder and shot. I have shot down many a deer that jumped up again and got clear. Now whenever you hear me fire one barrel, you will generally hear the other right after it. I don't take my gun from my face until I have fired both barrels, unless the first one tumbles him in a heap.

"There is something else that I think you don't know about—David does, I suppose, as he has killed a deer. Hunters have a custom of crowning a man when he shoots his first deer. I have known many quarrels to come from it. They don't crown them now, as that is rather too hard, but they smear the blood of the deer on his face. Now if either of you two shoots a deer, look out, for Mr. Pierce will put you through it. But I can tell you how you can escape. If you get to the deer first, bleed him and then stand over him and tell the first person who comes up to give you the cross. He will make a bloody cross on your forehead and you will have to wear it all day. That will clear you."

Mr. Hunter was a bit of a joker and liked some fun as well as anybody. But his story about the trick put upon young hunters was not altogether a joke. Many a spruce hunter has gone out with a party of rough hunters and, on killing his first deer, has been astonished and angered by their treatment. It is a custom more honored in the breach than in the observance and reminds one of the tricks sailors play on greenhorns who cross the line for the first time. Mr. Hunter had spoken of it in a grave manner, yet neither Mr. Hastings nor George felt that there was much danger of their being tricked. So Mr. Hastings merely laughed and shook his head as much as to say "they had better not try it on him." George said that when he found he had shot a deer he would be among the missing, and they would have a long run to catch him.

Mr. Hunter then proposed loading their guns as they might want to make a very early start in the morning and it would save time; "The dogs can trail so much better while the scent is fresh on the grass, than after it gets cold." He showed George how much powder to put in and how to chamber the buck shot, making them lie in regular layers so they scatter less. He then loaded his own heavy double barreled gun with great care, taking particular care to see that the tubes were filled with powder, instead of having only a few grains in them. "For," said he, "it vexes me so to have a gun snag."

"I thought," said Mr. Hastings, "that you old hunters disdained to hunt with anything but a rifle."

"I always used to," replied Mr. Hunter. "I never thought of using anything but a rifle. We used to call shotguns 'scatter guns' by way of contempt. But I have found that, though a rifle is best for some kinds of hunting, shot has great advantages. Having two barrels instead of one is a great thing and would have saved me a hard fight on one occasion."

"How was that?" asked Mr. Hastings.

"Well, I will tell you how it was. I was at work in a field at some distance from the house and suddenly made up my mind to go and try for a deer. I had left my hunting knife at home and did not want to go so far back for it, so I started on without it. I had two dogs with me, one a first rate deer dog, the other only a puppy that had been out but two or three times. I had not gone far when both of the dogs opened and Old Sam went off on a trail. The puppy seemed to be on another trail; and, from his movements, I thought was going to jump a deer. I ran for a stand and had just got there when a large buck came clipping through the palmettos. I fired at him and felt I had hit him, but he disappeared through the bushes. I did not stop to load my rifle but dove through the bushes after him, when what should I see but Mr. Buck with his feet planted and his hair all brushed up. As I came up, he came bulging at me perfectly mad.

"Now I was in my prime and I had a great idea of my strength. I knew there wasn't a man around that part of the country that was my better. So I dropped my gun and, as he came at me, I partly dodged him, caught him by the beams of his horns, and threw my whole weight on his neck, thinking I would get him down and hold him until my dogs came up. Well, I did throw him. But as to holding him, I found that I couldn't begin to do it. He threw me this way and that as though I was a child, and I hung on to his horns until the rough points had torn my hands so that blood streamed through my fingers. But I hung on and we tore over the ground, the old buck snorting and rolling his eyes fiercely at me until I began to get very tired. Then I thought that perhaps I might kick the wind out of him with my heavy shoes. So I watched for a chance and gave him powerful kick in the belly; and before you could snap your finger, he threw a complete somersault and took me along with him.

"I jumped up and tried to get out of his way, but he was just as quick as I was and came right at me again. All I could do was to seize him by the horns and at it we went again, tearing up the ground and struggling and straining, with me trying to keep his head down to the ground with my weight on it and him straining to gore and kick me. My puppy came up, but I could not get him to do anything; he was frightened and got out of the way. Oh, how I wished that Old Sam would come or that I had my knife. But my strength was failing and my breath came as if every one would be the last. I felt that I had got to do something and just then remembered having heard that if you can get a deer's foot over his horn, he is lost.

"I reached down and seized one of his fore legs and pulled it over his horn and then turned him loose. But he just threw his head on one side, his leg dropped out of his horn and he jumped up and came at me as fierce as ever. Well, I could do nothing but get him by the horns again and wrestle him down. And then I thought that if I could get both legs over his horns, I would have him. So after some hard work I got both his legs up over his horns and turned him loose again. Then I had him sure. He couldn't get up, anyway. He rolled his head and his eyes but it wasn't any use; he couldn't get his legs out of that hobble.

"I was trembling all over and looked about for a lightwood knot to knock him in the head, for I thought it was not worth while to load my rifle when I could knock him in the head. I found one, took a minute or so to catch my breath, and then drew off planning to give him a heavy lick between the eyes. But instead of knocking him between the eyes, the blow struck one of his horns and broke it off close up to his head, so that before I knew it he had his legs free and was on his feet and at me again.

"Well, I never was in another such a scrape in my life—I had only one horn to hold on by, while my knees trembled under me. But I got hold of the horn and then we had at it again. I had some advantage over him now, since he could not use his one horn as well as he had the two. But we fought and tore over a great space of ground, and I was just beginning to feel what I never did before or since, that my time was come, when I heard old Sam's voice close by in full yell on the buck's track. Oh, I never heard any music quite as sweet as that. I fought hard then, and Old Sam came tearing up and caught the Buck by his throat. Then I let go and lay down. I couldn't laugh but I lay there and chuckled to see the death grip Old Sam give him.

"Buck fought well, but it was of no use. Sam didn't let go of him until he laid still. Then the old fellow came to me wagging his tail and licking the blood off his chops, and looked as if he wanted to know if I was hurt. I tell you I had to hug that dog. Poor old fellow, the alligators got him at last. He ran a wounded deer off one day, and I suppose the deer took to the lake and Sam followed him and was picked up by an alligator. They were very thick over that way. At any rate, he never came back from the hunt. I felt almost as solemn about it as if I had lost one of my children, for I loved that dog.

"Well, as I was saying, ever since that buck fight I like to have two chances for a deer instead of one, and I tell you I never hunt without a good knife. A rifle is best for still hunting, and it is a little more pleasure to knock over your game with a simple ball. But sometimes a man has to shoot very quick and then a shotgun is best—especially if you have one that you can depend on, like Old Betsey there."

"Well, I know one thing," said George. "I shall never attack a wounded buck."

"You had better not. I really think a mad buck more dangerous than a bear or panther, not from that one fight alone but from other things I have seen and heard of. I was hunting once with a young man. He had wounded a buck and we were both following it up in hopes to find it or get another shot. He was ahead of me and the first thing he knew the buck was coming right at him, looking full of fight. He raised his rifle and fired but in his hurry missed him clear, and the buck kept right on. I saw his fix, whipped up my rifle and shot the buck right over his shoulder. It was close shooting, but I thought if the buck got to him, it would surely break some of his bones and I was confident of my skill in shooting. So, I tried it.

"I tell you, the fellow was frightened when he saw that he had missed the buck."

Shortly afterward, the young men retired to rest and all was quiet except the roaring of the wind in the tops of the pine trees and the barking of the dogs.

CHAPTER IV

THE RAIN — THE START — THE HUNT — THE RETURN
— STORIES ABOUT DEER — STORY OF THE BEAR HUNT
— THE STORM CONTINUES — THE RETURN HOME

Towards morning George awoke and was very disappointed at hearing the rain pattering on the roof. Mr. Hunter was already up and a large fire was blazing on the hearth. As soon as it was light, the three young men were astir. But on looking out, the prospects for a hunt seemed gloomy indeed. Mr. Hunter thought it might clear up after a while but more likely would rain by spells all day.

About nine o'clock Mr. Pierce came with five dogs. Since it had stopped raining, they decided to go although the rain would have spoiled the trails of the deer. George thought he had better not go, because he would get very wet and might take cold and injure his health. But Mr. Hunter told him he should have his horse and ride; they needed a horse in case they were successful and could bring home a deer. So George mounted the horse but would have preferred hunting on foot, as he did not think he could manage a horse and a gun well at the same time.

Mr. Hunter had two dogs. Dragon, an excellent hunting dog, was larger and heavier than a full blooded hound but had enough of the hound in him to make an excellent deer dog. The other dog, Ruler, was too young to be worth much and only on his second hunt. Mr. Hunter had a collar with a bell attached to it, which he always placed on Dragon for deer hunts. It often happens that a deer will run a long way after receiving a mortal wound, and Dragon would follow until he found it. But then he would lie down quietly by it and make no attempt to show where it was. The bell, however, would sound at every movement of his head. Mr. Hunter said that he would have lost many a deer if the bell had not been on Dragon.

As soon as Dragon heard the tinkling of his bell, he became almost frantic with joy and rushed into the house, barking and jumping up on Mr. Hunter. He knew he was wanted for a deer hunt and could hardly stand still long enough to have the collar fastened on his neck. The hunters now set out, with Mr. Hunter and Mr. Pierce sounding their horns, which drove the dogs almost crazy with excitement. But we will here give George's description of the hunt, which he wrote in a letter to his mother.

"We first went to a bay near the house. Mr. Hunter described the stands, that each of us were to go to. I being on horseback went to the farthest one, which I easily found, as the skull and horns of a buck had been placed on a stump, to mark it. Mr. Pierce went to a different part of the bay, with the dogs. Occasionally we could hear him whistling and encouraging the dogs to enter the bay. After quite a while spent here, he came through to me and said 'we will move on.' The dogs could not find any trails in that bay, though there was no doubt but that the deer were there. Mr. Pierce told me that I was at the stand where he had shot as many as twenty deer that had been run out of the bay. He then motioned to those who were in sight, to move on, and blew his horn, which soon brought the dogs about us.

"In this way we went, driving from different bays without jumping a deer. Once or twice, the dogs opened a few times, but the rain had spoiled the scent, so that they did not accomplish anything. Once they started, what Mr. Hunter said was a wild cat, and from the noise they made he judged that they had treed it, and were baying at it. But they called the dogs off and moved on again. I dismounted whenever I heard them open, for I did not want to shoot from a horse. Much of the time I was out of sight of the others. After a time we all got together at an old clearing and talked over affairs. Mr. Pierce said that the dogs had not been out in so long a time that they were too eager and overran the trails.

"Then we went to a large bay that they said they had never driven without starting a deer. Mr. Pierce took the dogs to one end of it, and we were posted across it, in a place where it was very narrow. It lay between two ranges of hills. I had a stand on the hill side and I waited there for more than an hour, occasionally hearing the dogs opening slowly as if on cold trails. Finally they seemed to go off out of hearing, and Mr. Hunter gave a whoop for us to come for him. He said that he was afraid we had all got tired of waiting so long a time, but that we might have some fun yet, for if the dogs did jump any deer in that bay, they were sure to run out this way.

"While we were talking over our ill luck, we heard the dogs in full cry coming towards us. We all ran for our stands again, but I got in a place where the palmettoe was so thick and high that the horse made his way with great difficulty through it; so I jumped off, and tied him to a tree, and ran for my stand. While I was there, Mr. Hunter and David both saw a deer run out of the bay and stop within fifty yards of me, but out of my sight owing to a hill which intervened. Mr. Hunter left his stand and tried to get within shot of him, but he appeared to scent danger at last, for he wheeled and went back into the bay, not far from where he came out.

"In a minute or two afterward the dogs ran two deer out at the stand that Mr. Hunter had just left, and we all saw them go up the hill side but were all too far off to shoot them. They ran through the pine woods and passed near Mr. Hunter's house. The boys at home had a good view of them. The deer that came out near me, must have heard the dogs, at a distance and ran out, though no dogs were on his trail. It now commenced to rain again, and after so much ill luck, we concluded to give it up, and try again the next day. So we went back to the house, and had a good dinner, and agreed to meet Mr. Pierce the next day, at a place where he said the chances were far better."

The evening after the hunt, everyone sat around a huge roaring fire, talking about the poor success they had met with and listening to Mr. Hunter's stories of hunting incidents.

"I lately read a piece in a newspaper," said Mr. Hastings, "that stated that while a doe has a young fawn too small to take care of itself, both the doe and fawn leave no trail scent for dogs to trail. It was said to be a wonderful provision of nature and was given on the authority of an old Canadian hunter. Do you know if it is so or not?"

"Well, I don't know anything about Canadian deer, for I have never seen them. But I know that the deer here always have a scent, for I have seen the dogs trail them. I have seen dogs trail young fawns and run them down, and I have seen them trail does that had fawns. I know it is not so here."

"I thought it very strange that I had never seen anything of the kind in books of natural history," said Mr. Hastings.

"Did you ever catch a young fawn alone?" asked George.

"Oh, yes! I have often caught them. We have had several that we kept about the house as pets, until after they were full grown. They are the most interesting creatures in the world; and you get so attached to them that I have said I would never have another one, for they are sure to get killed after a while. Then they are very troublesome; you can hardly make a fence about your garden high enough to keep them out. And when they get in, they nibble off the tops of everything. Then they will chew clothes that are hung out to dry. I have had them chew my shirts so as to spoil them. But they are very beautiful and cunning."

"How do the dogs agree with them?" asked David.

"Very well, except that the deer will sometimes plague the dogs. I have often seen one of our pet deer come out to where the dogs would be sleeping on the ground, run at them and strike them all with his fore feet and then run a little way and look back over his shoulder so much as to say, 'Come and catch me if you can.' The dogs would generally give a yelp and go and lie down in some other place; but the deer would come again, bush up his hair and strike the ground with his forefeet as if to challenge them. Then he would run at one of them and strike him again, and then turn and run away. So he would keep on plaguing the dogs until some of them would give a yell and start after him, when they would all rouse up and open, as if on a hunt; and away they would go on the full jump. Sometimes they would be gone half an hour, running all the time; and then the deer would come back and run into the house and generally under a bed or a table. Then he would put his head out and shake it at the dogs, who did not dare come into the house to meddle with him. I have seen them do that a number of times. The deer seem to like a chase once in a while."

"Oh, how I should like to have one to take home with me!" exclaimed George.

"I think it quite likely I could catch you one," said Mr. Hunter. "It will soon be time for them."

"I do wish you would. I would take a great deal of trouble to get one home safely. I would let a friend of mine who lives in the country keep it for me, as I could not keep it in the city."

"There is one thing about the very young ones that is a little singular," said Mr. Hunter. "I have found those that were too small to run much; and on picking them up, they would hang like a rag, as if there was no life in them. I would hold them up to my heart and pet them and carry them a half mile or so and then set them down, and they would trot along after me like little dogs. I think it is the scent of a man that frightens them so at first; and that after holding them and petting them awhile, they get used to it and get over their fright."

"I must have one if it is possible," said George. "How I should like to find one myself; it would give me a great deal of pleasure."

"If you can come out here, stay with me a while, and hunt and fish, you will stand a good chance for one."

"Well, I would like that first rate," said George. "But I must see what Uncle James says about it."

"You would have to take up with some pretty coarse fare and might get tired of it."

"Oh, I don't mind the coarse fare," replied George. "My physician said I needed a change of air and diet and living out here would be both. So it would be good for me for a while."

"Well, if you think you could be contented out here in the woods, why any time you will send me word, I will come over for you and you can have a horse most any time you want it to go to Welaka."

"I think I will come out for a short time, at any rate," said George.

"Well, you will probably have a shot at a bear too; towards spring they begin to come out and are very thick not far from here."

"I don't know as I want a shot at a bear. I heard a man tell such a terrible story about a bear fight that he was in that I think if they will let me alone, I will let them alone," replied George.

Mr. Hunter laughed. "Why, there is not much danger in a bear fight if you know how to manage. I have killed great numbers of them, and I think it is about the best sport I know of. Oh, I must have you on a bear hunt with me and show you some fun. It is pretty hard work, though, sometimes."

"Yes," said Mrs. Hunter who had been listening. "I have spent hours in picking the thorns out of his head after he has come from a bear hunt."

"A bear when he is hunted will always make for the thickest place he can find; and to get a shot at him you have go to follow. I always throw off my hat because I should lose it if I went in with it on and pitch in head first right after the bear."

"You must have had some pretty hard fights then," said Mr. Hastings. "Tell us one of them before we go to bed, and I will dream of hunting and fighting bears all night as I did of fighting a buck last night."

"Well, I don't know if it will be worth listening to, but I will tell you about the fight I had with the biggest bear I ever killed. One morning I was on my way to my field, when I was overtaken by a boy who had come to get me to go after a bear that had killed one of his grandfather's hogs. I had with me a good English musket, an old Revolutionary piece, that was very good; and I thought I would not go home for my rifle. I had my two dogs, Sam and Raymond, with me. They were the best bear dogs in the place; and, for this reason, I was often sent for to hunt bears that had been doing mischief. While the boy was after me, the old man had sent for some of his neighbors who came and all together we made a party of seven.

"At about half an hour by the sun, we set out for the place where the hog had been heard to squeal and soon found the hog partly eaten up. There was quite a number of dogs beside mine and they all commenced to eat the hog, but mine appeared at once to scent the bear and set off leaping over the high grass looking for him. They ran for a bay that was near and did not open as if on trail but seemed to wind him. In a few minutes we heard them yelling; and all ran to take stands around the bay except the Parson and I, who tried to follow the dogs.

"I ran into the bay a ways after the dogs and then I ran to a place where I thought I could head him right into the thickest place where they always try to get. I heard them coming towards me, crashing through the dead bay trees which had been burned and fallen down. Before he got to me, I found that he had changed his course and ran to head him. I saw him just as he was crawling over a high tussock[1]. I had not a good sight of him but I fired and struck him; he reared up and jumped right backwards among the dogs and then turned and kept on his course again.

"I did not stop to load up but ran out of the bay and around to the side I expected he would come out. While I was loading, he came out and one of the standers fired a small bored rifle at him and hit him. He ran across a narrow ridge of upland and into another thick bay—or rather a swamp—a desperate thick, tangled cypress swamp. By this time some of the other dogs had joined the chase. The man who had last fired took a double barreled shotgun from one of the others; and he, the Parson and I followed over into the swamp. I outran the others and got where I thought the dogs would come, and in a minute they came up.

---

1   A high bunch of briars and bushes.

"The bear was badly wounded and I was going slowly and the dogs were right at his heels. I fired again, and he ran a few steps and stopped to fight the dogs. I commenced loading and the Parson came up. I said, 'Give me your rifle and I will shoot him and you finish loading my musket.' I took the rifle and in trying to find an open place where I could shoot him, without killing some of the dogs, which were all about him, I got right in front of him. He threw the dogs off and rushed up towards me. I let him come to within four steps of me and then, as I raised the rifle up to shoot him, it went off before I had taken any aim. It was double triggered and had got out of order, which I did not know. I don't suppose I hit him, but he turned his course and ran into the edge of a lake that was near. The dogs stopped him again in a shallow place about knee deep, among the bonnets.

"I used a large Cuban yager ball, one of those that the Cuban filibusters who landed in Florida after their unsuccessful expedition had sold to help pay their expenses home. I put the ball on top of the charge of buckshot in my gun, and I ran up close to him and fired. The yager struck him in the lock of his jaws and broke down the lower jaw; and he came charging out of the water into a thick place nearby. I commenced loading my gun again; and, in doing so, I dropped all my buckshot into the water except three. I saw no one else, so I rammed them down and thought I would get as close as I could and fire them at him. As I came out of the water, I met the Parson again and he gave me eleven of his rifle balls, which I put on top of my buckshot. While I was looking for a place where I could see him, the Parson got a chance and fired. The bear ran out within a few steps of me and I fired the charge of buck shot and rifle balls plum into him.

"He roared out as a bear always roars when he has received his death wound—it was perfectly frightful—enough to make the hair stand on a man's head the way he pitched and tumbled and tore around roaring terrible all the time. I had no more shot to load with and, as soon as the Parson could load his rifle, I took that. The dogs were fighting him and were doing their best. Some that had not dared to go near him before were catching him. The bear appeared to be more ferverous than ever; he was wounded in the loins so that he had to drag himself with his forefeet, and his jaw was broken so that he could not bite. He would go a little way into the thickest places and then turn and come right back again, fighting the dogs with his forefeet all the time. I got down on my hands and knees and crawled through the thickets after him and shot him twice in the head as he was coming toward me but without any apparent effect. Just at this time the man that had the double barreled gun came up and the Parson commenced scolding him and asking him where he had been. He said he had got lost. We had heard him back in the swamp calling out, 'Don't shoot this way.'

"'Well, shoot that bear,' says the Parson. He fired both barrels into the bear's head, and it did not seem to make him wink from his numerous wounds.

"During the latter part of the fight, a thunder storm had been coming up; and it now burst upon us, the rain pouring in torrents with terrible thunder and lightning. Our guns were wet, so that after several attempts to fire them again we had to give it up. Then the Parson had got mad and drew his knife and said, 'Let's go at him with our knives.' I had all I could do to keep him from attacking the bear with his knife, as I knew the bear had life enough yet to rip him open with one stroke of his paw. All this time the dogs kept fighting the bear, and he kept growing weaker and weaker. At last, he raised himself up, threw his upper jaw on a white bay tree about the size of my leg that was bent down near the ground, bowed his back up apparently to get a purchase as his lower jaw was broke, and then threw himself back and tore a piece out of the tree a foot long and an inch deep at least. Then he stretched out, trembled all over and died.

"We skinned him, cut him up into quarters and carried him two miles, where we weighed him. The meat weighed five hundred and fifteen pounds. He was the largest bear and the blackest full grown bear I ever saw. I don't think you could have laid a dollar down on his skin anywhere from the middle of his body up to his ears without its covering one or more shot holes."

"You say the blackest full grown bear. Are not the full grown ones black?" asked Mr. Hastings.

"All the young ones are black, but the old ones are of a rusty brown color."

"Where is the best place to shoot a bear? In the head?" asked George.

"Oh, no. It is very hard to kill a bear by shooting him in the head. The right place to shoot a bear is about a hand's-breadth back of the shoulders and very low down. A bear's backbone is pretty nearly in the center of his body and the ribs rise up from it in an arc on each side. So if you shoot into the middle or upper part of his body, you don't hit any vital place. But if you shoot him low down just back of the forelegs, you shoot right into his vital parts, where they are not protected."

"I will remember that at any rate," said George.

They now retired, hoping that the morrow would be a clear day and that they would make up for their ill luck by a successful hunt. But they were doomed to disappointment again, for on arising in the morning they found it still looking stormy, as if it might rain at any moment. Then, too, one of the party on looking at his boots, which he had left by the fire to dry, found one of them so badly burned as to be of no further use. Having only a pair of light boots, which he could not hunt in the wet with, they all decided, much to Mr. Hunter's dissatisfaction, to start for home and try it again some other time.

So the house and cart were harnessed up and they set out for Welaka, which they reached without further incident. It was not very pleasant to return with no game, especially when they had fancied they would have at least one or two saddles of venison to bring home. But they were not discouraged. George seemed more eager than ever to hunt and said he should not rest until he had had some good hunting and had killed a deer.

CHAPTER V

AMUSEMENTS — A SCHOONER FOR CATTLE — EXCELLENT

FINDING — SAILING — VISIT A LOGGING CAMP — A BEAR

CHASE — ANZIE ISLAND — ATTEMPT TO REACH SILVER

SPRING — CAMP ON LAKE GEORGE — FIRE HUNT — HEAD

WIND — RUN ASHORE — ORANGE POINT — SAIL FOR HOME

Shortly after George had returned from Mr. Hunter's, Uncle James told him that he was planning a trip to New Orleans. Since his nephew had made so many friends and enjoyed himself so much at Welaka, he had been thinking of leaving him there. Said he, "I shall be absent about five or six weeks; and after I return, we will visit Enterprise and St. Augustine."

George had been enjoying himself very much. He had formed a close friendship with David and had a number of others. His frank, gentlemanly manners made everyone who became acquainted with him like him. His evenings were especially delightful. Since a number of gentlemen and lady boarders at the house were good musicians, an evening seldom passed without vocal and instrumental music. David played very fairly on the flute, and George played the violin very well. He borrowed one from one of the neighbors for amateur concerts that would put to the blush many a city entertainment. They also had a number of pleasant moonlight excursions on the river and enjoyed themselves together without stiffness or constraint.

When it appeared, the steamboat which would take Uncle James down the river had a schooner in tow to load with cattle. This was quite an event in the village. Everyone wondered when and where and how the cattle were to be brought and loaded. Captain Ambler from the schooner was a young man, a native of Connecticut, who had gone to sea early. Although he had commanded the schooner for some years, this was his first voyage for cattle and he said he knew nothing about loading them as he had never seen it done. He seemed to anticipate a very disagreeable job. A merry, good natured man full of songs and stories, he and George soon became well acquainted.

Captain Ambler went with George and David to troll one day and they had very good success. The trout, out in the deep water attacking a school of silver fish, were constantly striking all about the boat. David and the captain each pulled an oar with one hand and held a line with the other, while George steered the boat and also held a line. They rowed round and round in a circle about fifty yards in diameter. Sometimes all three would be pulling in a fish at the same time. After they had caught about twenty, David and Captain Ambler ceased catching any. Then five times in succession, as the boat reached the same place in the circle, George drew in a fish.

"Well, you're in luck," said the captain.

"It is a little singular," said David, "that they should strike so many times just at that spot and at George's line only."

"Oh, it's all luck, all luck," said the captain.

"I don't know about that," said David. "George's spinner is different from either yours or mine and that may be why they bite at his line and not at ours. Then the sun must strike full on it, just as we are in that place. You can see from the position of the sun that it must; that may account for his catching them just in the same spot. When I see luck go to such an extent, I always think there is some very good reason for it, which we may not know."

"Oh, of course they bite better at some tackle than at others. But then I have fished many a time with a party all having the same kind of bait and lines; and one or two would catch a great many, and the others not get even a bite even though they changed places with the lucky ones."

"Yes. I know it happens so sometimes, but, perhaps, if you had examined every thing, some difference in tackle or bait would have accounted for it."

Since the fish seemed to have stopped biting, they rowed home. They had twenty-five fish weighing from one to six pounds apiece, so they sent some to the neighbors. The captain invited David and George to come and dine with him the next day. His cook, he said, could make an excellent chowder.

They went down the next day and found the chowder to be as the captain said. He told them that he had expected to have shipped the cattle at Smyrna down the coast. But when he arrived off Smyrna, he could get no pilot to take him in. While waiting there, he was caught in a storm, dismasted, and obliged to go back to Savannah for repairs. The cattle which had been collected for him were turned out into the woods again. Now the schooner had come up to Welaka but all the cattle were still scattered, though there were a number of men out hunting them. Still it would probably be two weeks before they would be at Welaka. In the meantime the captain was preparing everything that he thought would be needed. The schooner was hauled close to the shore at a place where the bank was steep and high and where a strong staging with high sides would connect a cattle pen, built for the occasion, with his vessel. And his crew had cut pine saplings to tie the cattle and lashed them through the vessel both in the hold and on deck. After showing them all these arrangements, the captain proposed that they take a sail in his boat.

The boat was a large yawl capable of holding twenty men with ease and rigged with a jib and mainsail. They took their trolling lines with them and sailed down the river to the point where they caught so many fish the day before. Although the trout were striking, the wind would not allow them to sail just where they wished. So they caught but eight. While they were returning, the captain proposed that on the next day they should go in his boat down the river to General H's logging camp. The general, who lived at Welaka, had a logging camp about four miles below and had invited them to visit whenever they wished.

The next morning, a Saturday, they set sail for the logging camp. The party consisted of the captain, George, David and the general's two sons. They had a pleasant sail, shooting a number of ducks with the guns they had brought. On arriving at the camp, the general received them warmly and set his cook at work to get up a good dinner for them. The camp consisted of four large tents: one for himself, two for his negroes, and the fourth for keeping stores and fodder.

After looking at the camp, they walked down the river a short distance to the landing to see part of a raft of logs, then followed the log road out through the hammock to the pine woods where the negroes were cutting down the great pine trees. After being felled, the trees are cut into proper lengths and then swung into a cart with very large wheels. Pairs of mules, varying in number according to the state of the road and the size of the logs, haul the logs to the landing where they are rolled into the water and secured by looms until enough have been gathered to form a section of a raft.

After dinner, the general told them that the wind had died away and that they had better take down their mast and sails. Since he and his hands were going up to Welaka, they would all go together in the captain's boat, which his negroes would row. When Captain Ambler saw that it was as calm as the general had said, he gladly consented to the arrangement. At about four o'clock all was ready, and they got into the boat. The general's two boys and Uncle Jack sat in the bow. Then four strong negroes, each with a good oar, filled the middle; and the general, the captain, David, and George sat in the stern. The negroes made the boat move rapidly; and, as the weather was delightful, they enjoyed it very much.

Just as they turned around a point of land, Uncle Jack sang out, "Look dah. See de bar swimmin' over de river." They all looked and, sure enough, there was a bear about a half a mile from them just starting to swim across the river.

"Pull—boys—pull!" shouted the general. "Here, captain, let me steer. You take a gun. Boys, load up, all of you with a good bear load. If we can only head him, we will give him a whole broadside."

The negroes bent to their oars, and the boat jumped through the water at every stroke. Those who had guns loaded them with buck shot; but, by the time they were prepared, the chase was drawing to a close.

"I am afraid he is going to get away," said the general. "He has not far to go now and he sees us and is doing his best. Pull, boys, hard, just a minute or two longer."

The negroes strained every muscle and the boat gained on the bear.

"Now, boys, be ready. When I say, 'Fire!', give it to him and then look out for yourselves and drop down low. I think I will have to let the boat swing into that low tree there if I head him off."

Another moment and they were within thirty feet of the bear and running straight towards him. The general put the helm down and, as the boat swung around, cried "Fire!" Four guns went off almost together, all aimed at poor Bruin's head. The next moment the boat went crashing into the tree beyond, which projected out from the bank. Since some of the party had been so anxious to see the effects of their shot that they had forgotten to dodge down, they were knocked over in the boat. A few light scratches and bruises were the only evil results. When they came to look about for the bear, they found that one of the negroes had caught him by the ears and was holding on to him. Backing the boat out from under the tree, they hauled it in. He was a young one, and they had peppered his head so full of buck shot that it killed him instantly. After clearing the broken limbs and leaves out of the boat, they rowed on again.

Meanwhile, the tongues of the young men had not been silent. They shouted as they gained on the bear and as they fired their guns. When they were knocked over by the tree limbs, they laughed at the ludicrous positions in which they found themselves, some of them sprawling in the bottom of the boat.

"Who killed the bear? That is the question," said the captain.

"I think the honors are divided among you," replied the general. "You can each of you say that you shot a bear; for if any of you missed him at that distance, you ought to be scrubbed up with black jack."

George was very interested in examining the bear. He remarked its small ears and tail—its muscular forelegs, broad back and strong sharp claws. While he had been very excited during the chase and at the time the bear was killed, being in the stern of the boat he had seen the tree and had dodged it. On reaching home the general had the bear cut up and sent pieces of it to the captain and to the boarding house so that George had his first taste of bear meat. He thought it very good, by way of variety. As to killing it, he felt very pleased at having had a hand in the hunt, although he did not think it was a thing to brag of as they had every advantage of the poor creature.

A few days afterward, Mr. Brown, David and George went with the captain in his boat up to Anzie Island, where they were pleasantly received and feasted on delicious oranges. On their return the wind all died away and they were left to float home with the current or to row with the heavy oars. Because it was a lovely evening, they rowed only across the lake and let the current take them to Welaka. The captain sang songs, with the others joining in the chorus until they reached home at bed time.

On the way home, Mr. Brown, who lived at Welaka, proposed that they should get up an excursion to Silver Spring near the western shore of Lake George. The spring was said to be a great natural curiosity, but few people visited it because of the difficulty of reaching it. There was no settlement within ten miles of it; in fact, the whole western shore of Lake George was uninhabited. The captain said he could not go, as they might be gone several days and he was expecting the cattle to arrive every day. But he told them that they were welcome to the use of his boat. George and David were delighted with the idea. Mr. Brown proposed that they should ask Captain Stebbins to go, as he was a good hunter, knew the way to the spring, and knew where the best camping places and orange groves were. The day after their return, they saw Captain Stebbins, who agreed to go with them. They also invited several other people and decided to start on the next morning, if the weather proved favorable.

The next morning was a pleasant one. Since George and David had made all their preparations the previous evening, they were early at the wharf and had their luggage in the boat and the boat in readiness before the others appeared. Mr. Brown and Captain Stebbins arrived soon after and then they waited an hour for the others. When no one else came, they set sail without them as they did not want to lose any more of the favorable wind. They took with them such eatables as they thought best and things necessary for cooking game and fish, as well as guns, trolling lines, axes, a frying pan, and a coffee pot.

They had to beat up to the point at Welaka, then enter Little Lake George, across which they dashed rapidly. Beyond this the river was narrow and crooked for a few miles, and they advanced slowly until they again entered a wide expansion of the river. There, the wind not being broken by the trees on shore drove them along until they had gone twelve miles from home. The wind gradually abated and they found they would have to row. The oars were large and heavy and they took turns at them, but it was late in the afternoon when they reached the entrance to Lake George with the spring ten miles farther on. So they gave up the idea of reaching it that might and, by Captain Stebbins' advice, steered for Wilkie Point, opposite the western end of Anzie Island.

Wilkie Point was once occupied by a man named Wilkie, who built a home, cleared some land and grafted many of the sour orange trees. When he died, his house burned down and the place had never been occupied since. The grafts in the trees grew, along with the original growth. Though the trees bore thousands of sweet oranges, they could only be picked with difficulty as they were so mingled with the sour ones. Captain Stebbins said that he had already taken some from there that season and supposed that the grove had already been well gleaned. Still, he thought they could find enough to pay for the trouble of looking. Since the land was dry with plenty of lightwood near for their fire, it would be a good place to camp for the night. He thought too of going on a fire-hunt that night, as it was a good place for a deer and there was also a chance to get a turkey in the morning.

So many favorable things combining, they steered for the point and, rounding the end of it, ran the boat on a sandy beach which the captain pointed out. In a few minutes they dispersed through the grove, looking for sweet oranges. They all met with poor success, however, except the captain, for the sweet oranges looked so much like the sour ones that only someone used to distinguishing between them could readily do so. Only on comparing them carefully is the difference easily perceived. The sweet orange has a lighter color and much smoother skin than the wild orange. But the dark leaves were so thick and the untrimmed trees so brushy that George, after hunting for some time and only finding two, went back to the boat. The others soon came, Captain Stebbins with his pockets full of oranges which he distributed among them.

They now began unloading the boat and building a tent for the night. Mr. Brown and Captain Stebbins took the mast and sails out of the boat. They found a tree with a crotch in it and near it drove into the ground a forked stake of the same height, putting one end of the mast through the crotch of the tree and the other on the stake. The tree, being firm, gave a stability to the frame, which the stake would not have. The long oars and poles were then laid with one end on the mast and the other on the ground to form the frame. Because the main sail just covered the top and one end, they used the jib to fill up the other end. Thus they had a comfortable tent that would run rain. Cutting palmetto leaves, they spread them over the ground to form a bed. The captain took one of the axes and went for lightwood, soon returning with a quantity.

Since they had eaten only a lunch since morning, they set about preparing a hearty meal. One of the two trout which George had taken with his troll was soon in the frying pan. Two boat seats were placed on a frame to serve as a table and others fixed on either side for seats. It was dark before supper was ready, so Mr. Brown cut a green bush and trimmed it up, leaving a number of forks in it. Sticking it in the ground near the table, he put some pieces of lightwood in it and set them on fire so the bush could serve as a candlestick. Using your ingenuity to furnish rough substitutes for the various comforts of home life is one of the greatest pleasures of camp life. They enjoyed their meal of fish, roast potatoes, bread and butter, and coffee, eaten by torch light and starlight in the edge of a thick grove where they could hear the low murmur of the waves as they rippled on shore.

After supper, the captain said that it was just the night for a fire hunt and proposed that he and David should go. George wished to join them, but the captain told him that they had a very wet boggy place to cross and would probably get wet to their knees, so he decided to stay in camp. Since the moon would rise at about ten that night, it would just suit them If they were successful, they could be back by then. The captain cut some lightwood into small pieces, put them in a bag, and lashed a stick to the handle of the frying pan. He carried the pan filled with fire over his left shoulder, moving it about with his left arm while using his right arm and both hands to hold and direct his gun. David was to follow, carrying the bag and keeping in his shadow, only coming up to him when the fire needed replenishing.

Mr. Brown cleared the table and hung their eatables where he thought no prowling animals could get them. Finding that the tent needed something for pillows, he and George made a torch of lightwood splinters, threw more wood on the fire to have a bright beacon to guide them back to camp and then set out to gather moss. The grove was a thick one, impassable where there was undergrowth except by the trails that cattle and hogs had made and which crossed each other in every direction. George held the torch in one hand and carried the moss which Mr. Brown pulled from the trees in the other. The moss was thin and scattered on these small trees. If they had been near larger ones, they could have collected all they needed in a few minutes. They brought several armfuls to the camp and found their fire of great use in directing them through the confusing, crooked paths. As they were pulling moss from one tree, they frightened a number of roosting birds and a great owl suddenly flew out of it, making a great noise with his wings. After they had done everything they could think of to make themselves comfortable, George and Mr. Brown lay down in their tent. They had lain but a few minutes when they heard two reports of a gun. Hoping that the captain had been fortunate, they continued talking for an hour when he and David returned.

"Well, where is your deer?" asked Mr. Brown.

"Out in the woods," replied the captain.

"Why didn't you bring him home?"

"Well, we have had a pretty hard time. We went a long way before we saw anything but cattle. Then I shone a deer's eyes and after a time got near enough to shoot. I gave him both barrels and there was a great kicking. I think I threw him, but when we got there he was gone. We followed the blood a little way, but it was too thick a place to do anything at night. If you and I go early in the morning, I think we can find him."

David was very wet and tired, for he had slipped in the dark. He said he was glad George did not go with them as there had been no fun in tramping through the swamps and thickets, getting wet and scratched and not bringing anything home.

They all lay down to sleep. Though the mosquitoes, attracted by the fire, troubled them some, George had a good night's sleep. Once he awoke and thought he heard some animal walking through the grove near them. While he was listening and thinking of awakening the captain, Mr. Brown got up and walked out of the tent with his gun. After throwing some fresh fuel on the fire and examining the gun's loads, he disappeared into the grove. George lay still, thinking that he would seize his gun and follow at the next sound. But he heard nothing. When Mr. Brown came back in a few minutes, George asked if he had seen anything. He replied that it was a cow in the grove; he had heard it and thought it might be a bear, as they were often seen swimming the river between this point and the island.

George did not awake again until daybreak. He walked to the boat and looked out on the lake, where a light fog was hanging over one side while toward the east a clear sky was just faintly tinted with the beams of the rising sun. As the captain joined him, he heard a strange wailing cry that seemed at a great distance.

"What is that noise?" he asked.

"I heard a wolf cry just now. Do you mean that?"

"Yes, I suppose it was a wolf; I never heard one before. What a dismal sound it is."

"It is more dismal when they are close to you. I think that one is on the other side of the lake. If so, he is ten minutes from us at least. But this little breeze is just right to bring the sound. I think we shall have wind from the South today and plenty of it too. If we do, we may not be able to reach the spring unless we camp another night."

In a few minutes the captain and Mr. Brown set out to try and find the deer that had been wounded the night before. George and David set to work striking the tent and getting everything in the boat. They shoved off until only her bow touched shore a little, then rolled up blankets, took down their tent and stowed everything in its place except what they would need for breakfast and the mast and sail, which were too heavy for them to handle.

"There," said David, "we can get off now as soon as we have eaten breakfast."

"Yes," said George, "and we ought to get off pretty soon, too, if we expect to get to the spring, for we shall have to beat there against a head wind. Well, if it holds, it will be just what we want to go home with. That is some consolation."

They now set to work preparing breakfast. They cooked the other fish that George had caught, washed the potatoes, made coffee, and soon had all things ready. They had just completed their preparations when the others returned, and they returned apparently with no game.

"What, no deer?" exclaimed George. "That is too bad, but it does seem as if no one will have any success hunting when I am in the party."

"We found the place where the deer was shot and think he was badly wounded, but we can't track him through the thickets and bogs. If we had had a dog, we could find him. But as we had not and were pushed for time, we gave it up and the buzzards will get him, I suppose. But look behind the palmettos there, George."

George looked and found two wild turkeys they had shot.

"Hurrah! Why, that gobbler is a splendid fellow. See the green and gold feathers how they glitter."

"Shall we have some fried turkey for breakfast?" asked the captain.

"I think we had better not wait to do so," said Mr. Brown. "Let us get under way as soon as possible."

After breakfast, they stepped the mast, put the remaining things on board, shoved off and got under way. There was a good breeze but from the worst possible quarter. They tacked over to the island and back, without making much way. But their next tack carried them out into the lake, and they decided to make a long one and cross to the eastern shore. The wind kept increasing and the waves began to get very large, but their boat was large and so strong they thought it could stand anything they would meet. They made a tack about twelve miles in length and then went about, hoping to make the mouth of the creek that flows from the spring.

As they raced along with the wind increasing steadily and the waves so high that they kept tossing the boat around, they saw an immense flock of wild ducks and in a few minutes were among them. Because the waves were so high, many of the ducks, after various ineffectual attempts to rise, would dive. The boys got their guns out, but the boat's rapid shifts made it impossible to take aim. They shot a few, but could not stop to pick them up without losing too much time, so they did not try to kill any more. Mr. Brown, who sailed the boat, said they would have to go ashore and reef the sail, as he was getting afraid that the boat could not stand up under the full sail. They found that they could not get within four or five miles of the spring on that tack and could only make Yellow Bluff, a high yellow sand bank or bluff. The captain said its shallow water made it a poor place to land, but they could do no better without losing time. So they ran the boat boldly toward the shore. She struck on sand bars a number of times, but the waves were so high that they carried her over and soon brought up close to the shore.

They reefed the sail and then held a council to decide what to do. It would be pretty late in the afternoon before they could get to the spring, and then they would want two or three hours to see the spring and to get oranges. That would oblige them to camp out another night. Since the next day was Sunday, they did not want to stay. The captain said that there was an orange grove four or five miles from where they then were and directly on the route home. He thought they could get as many bitter sweets there as they wanted. Since the wind was so fair for a quick trip home, he favored going home. Mr. Brown said that the wind was increasing all the time and he did not know how much the boat would stand and had rather not beat against it any more. David and George agreed, saying, "Well, let us go home then and try it again when we have the whole week before us to stay."

They got the boat afloat again and, turning their course nearly before the wind, started moving at a tremendous rate; in a few minutes they ran five miles and landed on Orange Point. Seeing nothing but cabbage palmetto trees along the shore, they walked through them until they came to a large orange grove. But someone had been there before them and stripped the bitter sweet trees. They got about a hundred, however, and then set sail for home. From Orange Point to Rocky Point, then to Wilkie Point, and then they were out of the lake and in the river where the wind and waves were not so high. The wind held and they ran all the way home in fine style, reaching the wharf at four in the afternoon. They had sailed about sixty miles altogether and were well pleased with their excursion, although they had not attained their main object. They all intended to try it again. Since the following day was stormy, they were very glad that they had not remained in camp another night.

CHAPTER VI

ARRIVAL OF THE CATTLE — HOISTING THEM IN THE HOUSE — ACCIDENTS AND INCIDENTS — VISIT CAPTAIN S. — RELICS OF THE FLORIDA WAR — SQUIRREL HUNTS — PAT GETS PERFUMED — A GOPHER — BLIND MOSQUITOES ETC. — WOODS ON FIRE — A HUNT IN THE SWAMP — VISIT MR. HUNTER

They had expected to see Captain Ambler's drove of cattle on their return but found they had not yet arrived. On Sunday afternoon, however, George heard a singular kind of shouting. Looking at the road along the river, he saw a great cloud of dust and at once realized that the cattle were coming. As he walked down to see them, the drovers were just turning them into a large enclosure. The herd were all steers and most of them large, well proportioned animals. But they had been driven ten days with nothing to eat except what they picked up along the road and so looked very hollow and sunken.

Stock raising is an important business in Florida. Some of the stock-owners have great numbers of cattle; the most we have heard of any one man owning is six thousand. Owners brand their herd with a design which consists of letters or figures and must be registered to be lawful. Each owner hunts cattle from the woods and swamps in the spring and brings them to pens where the calves are marked by notches in their ears and the yearlings branded. Then most cattle are let out to feed during the day, while the calves remain penned up. At night all the grazing cattle return to the pens, while the calves are let out. This goes on for several months until the new spring grass begins to fail or the range has been eaten, when the cattlemen turn them out again to wander where they like. Those which have been penned up will generally herd together the rest of the year.

Florida ships a great many cattle every year to the West Indies, Charleston and Savannah. Since the cattle have been in the woods so much of the time, they tend to be very wild. They can be managed, however, by those who understand them. Drovers always go on horseback and each one carries a whip with a short handle and a very long lash. They can crack or pop these whips as loud as a pistol. While driving cattle, they generally keep up such an incessant cracking that they have been nick-named "crackers," a term villagers now use as nickname for all country people. The drovers' horses are generally well trained, often chasing cattle which make a dash to break away from the herd.

Early Monday morning George went down to the wharf to see what was being done. He found that the drovers had gotten all the cattle into the pen and were about to take them on board. One of the drovers took a noose with a long rope attached to it and walked over the staging into the pen; there he used a pole to spread the noose and, walking around the moving cattle, he watched his opportunity, cast his rope over the broad horns of one, and shouted, "Pull!" The sailors at once pulled on the rope which tightened the noose and forced the poor beast through the pen and over the staging to the side of the schooner. There they hooked hoisting tackle to the noose and the poor brute was swung up by his horns over the hatch-way and lowered down into the hold.

While they were hoisting each cow up, the rope, still fast to the noose, was passed to men in the hold. As soon as it landed in the hold, sailors unhooked the tackle and used the rope to make the cow walk to its place in the stronghold, where it was tied by another short rope to poles put up for that purpose. Since the sailors were hoisting the cattle in at the forward hatch, George, Mr. Brown and some others sat on the roof of the caboose, from which they had good view of all the operations. Some of the ladies came down and sat in the upper story of the store to look at this unusual scene, and many of the country people came in to see the sight.

Sometimes it would be a long while before the drovers could get one of the cattle lassoed, because they rushed around so wildly that the man responsible was afraid to go near them. He also had to use a heavy rope so it would be strong enough to hoist the cattle, which made working with it more difficult. Some cows would dash about furiously when they found a rope on their horns or plant their feet firmly, holding back with all their strength, so that it took four men to pull them slowly forward. To such fellows they would hitch a tackle. The floor of one end of the staging rested on the gunwale of the vessel where, just at the side of the schooner, the tackle was hitched onto the cattle.

The cattle all held back so hard that no one thought it necessary to bar up the inner end of the staging. But bye and bye a fierce old fellow seemed to think they had hauled on his horns long enough. Since he found it was of no use to hold back, he started to go ahead. And go ahead he did. The sailors tumbled over one another in their haste to get out of the way and the steer clambered over them. After he stepped on one of them without hurting him much, the sailors jumped into the rigging while the steer kicked around on a deck filled with water casks, coils of rope, and spars. Finally, one of the sailors, getting hold of the end of his noose, hooked on the tackle. Before Mr. Steer knew what was the matter, his head was going up; and though he kicked and fought well, still up and up he went until he swung over the hatchway, when they lowered him and he found himself on his side in the hold.

After that, the inward end of the staging was kept barred until each cow began to rise off its fore feet. Another time, as the sailors were hoisting one up, he swung right amongst them, kicking out with all four feet and twirling round. This was so unexpected an attack that they all had to let go and he crashed down on the deck. But the sailors soon got hold of the rope and swayed him up again.

After witnessing the loading on deck, George went below to see what was happening. The difficulty there was to make the cattle go just where they were wanted. Coming from the light into a comparatively dark place and having just passed through such a rough experience, some cattle were too frightened and some too ugly to mind. Since there was no door to escape, the men had to be very careful to secure them so they could not attack anyone. Some seemed furious and ready to charge anybody; others were quiet enough. Then several that had been tied to their places got loose; and the sailors had pretty warm work of it, dodging around masts.

The cattle were wild and, though starving, few would eat hay. Some of Florida's wild cattle will not eat hay or any kind of feed unless trained to do so. Captain Ambler had been told that they would eat the moss which hung from the trees all about; in fact, it was a part of their usual food. So the captain had all the boys in the place gather green moss. George, getting a little, thought he would see if they would actually eat it. Most of them were too afraid, but some were eager for it. In a short time, all were reaching out their tongues and heads for it. One of the men brought them a bucket of water, but the smell of the tarred rope handle frightened them so they would not touch it, until the bucket was pulled up against their noses. Once they felt the water, they would drink as long as any remained.

It took two days to get the hold filled. Then the crew roofed over a part of the deck with a temporary shed that had been already prepared. By this time the sailors had learned how to handle the cattle quicker and better. Everything worked smoother except that two in the hold had lain down. Because they were probably injured internally from their struggles, they were hoisted out and sold cheaply to some of the country people who hoped they would recover. The cattle on deck stood with their heads over the sides and had plenty of fresh air; and the sailors rigged a sort of rack to put their feed in. After several more days of preparations, the schooner was again taken in tow by the steamboat for her trip to Guadalupe. George never learned how many cattle lived through the voyage.

Captain Stebbins had invited George and David to come to his house about two miles from Welaka and see him, promising to show them a number of Indian curiosities he had gathered while captain of a volunteer company in the late Indian War. One day George and David agreed to pay him a little visit. David took his rifle and a black terrier dog called Pat, thinking they would do some squirrel hunting since Pat was good at treeing squirrels if nothing else. They were pleasantly received and, after a while, George asked about the Indian curiosities. Laying them out for his inspection, the captain showed him a belt and hunting pouch that had belonged to the celebrated chief Billy Bowlegs. A complete set of his holiday attire was captured by one of the expeditions the captain had accompanied. The belt and bag, fancifully ornamented by beads, were evidently intended to be worn only on grand occasions.

But the most interesting article was the buckskin hunting shirt that had been worn by an Indian whom Captain Stebbins had shot. It was of enormous breadth, and the captain said that the man who wore it, a very large, powerful Indian, was evidently a doctor or "medicine man," based on the content of his bags and pouches. George found examining it both interesting and yet somewhat horrible, especially seeing the hole where the ball that killed him passed through. He had two leather pouches or bags, one containing his ammunition and the other a number of small packages of paints, roots and powders. He also had a little wickerwork box or basket filled with the down of some bird for stopping gunshot wounds and many strange things tied up in pieces of rag and buckskin. The captain showed them a string of large, heavy blue glass beads on a throng of buckskin, three yards long, which he wore in a number of folds around his neck. His rifle had been restocked by the Indians in imitation of the former stock, the little ornaments of which had been preserved and fastened to the new work. The captain's stories of the Indian War interested them very much.

In the afternoon they went down into a hammock on the side of the river to shoot what Floridians call cat-squirrels but are known as grey squirrels in the north. Florida also has fox-squirrels, the largest of all squirrels, found not in swamps but in pine woods. The captain took a dog that was good for squirrels and David had Pat. But the dogs would not help much, since the trees were so thick that the squirrels seldom came down on the ground but leaped from tree to tree. The captain called George's attention to the regular ridges all through the hammock, showing that it had been cultivated at some former time, probably by the Spanish, though now it had trees apparently of a century's growth.

Their dogs now barked most of the time, but the trees were so dense that it was difficult to see the squirrels, which could hide away in a very small place. David followed the dogs through the hammock, while the captain and George thought they would stand still, knowing there must be squirrels all about them. Presently they saw one jump, and the captain fired a rifle ball through his head. In a few minutes they saw another jump on a large tree, but the captain lost sight of him. He told George to take his rifle and watch for the squirrel, while he went to the other side to throw up clubs to drive him to change position. Presently the little fellow came running around the body of the tree; when he stopped, George dropped him, although not very scientifically. Instead of hitting him in the head, he hit his shoulder and tore the body badly.

They kept on through the hammock until the sun was going down, when, having game enough, they turned toward the house again. It seemed a pity to kill such lively graceful little creatures, but grey squirrels are excellent eating. And in a new country the only delicacies people have are the small game which generally abounds there. They spent the night at the captain's house and listened to his stories about the latter part of the Florida War. The next morning they started for home but went a long route through the pines, hoping to shoot some fox-squirrels to make a squirrel pie.

Pat was lively and dashed through the woods with his nose searching for tracks, disappearing often behind small hills. After a time they heard his sharp bark and, following the sound, soon saw him sitting on the ground looking up into a large pine tree. After some time looking, they discovered the squirrel high up in the top of it. George took the rifle, made an excellent shot, and the squirrel came flying through the air. The moment he touched the ground, Pat had him but the boys beat their dog off since the squirrel was already dead. As they walked through some tall grass, Pat began barking furiously. George, who caught a glimpse of some animal near Pat, was just about to run up and see what it was when David called to him to hold on because it was a polecat. The next minute its tail disappeared down a gopher hole. Coming nearer, they saw poor Pat scrubbing his head in the sand and were saluted with such an offensive odor that they were glad to make a hasty retreat.

Pat appeared to be in a great deal of trouble; he would put his head down on the ground and then shove himself along by his hind legs to try and get the odor off. The boys thought their squirrel hunting was at an end, since it seemed impossible that Pat should now trail anything by its scent. But soon they were surprised to hear his cheerful bark again and, going to a tree, found a squirrel in it, which David shot. Pat tried again at a black jack (black oak) tree not more than twenty feet high. Since there was a large pine tree near it, both boys looked only carelessly at the small tree, thinking the squirrel had run up the pine.

After looking until their eyes ached and not seeing any squirrel, they were about to give up when George raised his eyes along the lower limb of the black jack. There, almost within reach of his rifle was a black squirrel, nearly the color of the tree and so low down that they had overlooked him. George took the rifle and thought he could hit him exactly in the eye but made a very poor shot. The squirrel ran up the big pine and hid so cleverly in the straw that they could see only a little portion of his body. They fired three or four shots at him before he came down. Having secured as many squirrels as they wanted, they now turned directly towards home.

On the way, hearing Pat barking furiously again, they went to see what he had found. As they came up to the dog, David said, "It was only a gopher."

"A gopher," exclaimed George, "why that is just what I have been wanting to see for a long time. I have seen so many of their holes all about that I am anxious to see one."

"Well there he is," said David. "Take a good look at him."

"Yes, he looks like a large land turtle or tortoise; only his shell is very arched and his body much thicker between the two shells. There he is walking! Oh, how high he stands. Why, he seems to walk on the tip ends of his feet!"

The gopher, about a foot in length, walked along at a quick rate on the ends of his feet, which were much longer in proportion than those of a tortoise. Gopher holes appear all about the woods. About ten inches wide and arched like the gopher's back, they descend into the ground at a 45° angle and are so large at bottom that foxes often go into them when pressed by dogs. Since horses often stumble into them, they avoid them whenever possible.

Among the many things which George saw in Florida that were new to him were blind mosquitoes, sand flies, wood ticks, and red bugs. Blind mosquitoes make their appearance on the banks of the St. Johns River in countless millions, although they last but a few weeks. They are about the size of ordinary mosquitoes, slow in their movements and do not bite. It is said that they can often be seen advancing from the river in such numbers that they look like a cloud or fog coming. While they settle on bushes and trees along the river's bank, they never seem to go back into the country. At night they pour into open windows if there is a light in the room and fly into the light in such numbers as to put it out. They are especially troublesome for anyone walking through bushes, because they swarm into people's faces. At sunset they sang so loudly that George was reminded of large steamboats blowing off steam.

Sand flies are small gnats that come in great quantities during the spring wherever there are large bodies of water. About three o'clock each afternoon they swarm around houses, sometimes in such numbers that the only way of escaping them is to cover up one's face and hands or else to build a fire so the smoke will drive them away. They often last through the months of March and April.

Wood ticks, small insects that get on people walking through grass or bushes, bury their heads in the flesh and grow astonishingly large rapidly. They are very painful and difficult to remove after they have taken a firm hold. Bed bugs are similar, except that they are red and so small that they can hardly be seen. Without care and cleanliness, these fleas will make any place too hot for anyone except such thick skinned persons as mind nothing of the kind.

But George did not suffer much from any of these annoyances. Occasionally he would find a tick on one of his arms, but the sand flies had not yet come and the house where he boarded was kept so neat that fleas seldom troubled him.

One day George and Mr. Brown were fishing down the river in a boat. Since the air had been filled with smoke and cinders for several days, everyone knew that the woods were on fire in the country back of Welaka. Mr. Brown told George that the wind had changed during the morning, and he thought the fire would soon reach the village. Looking in that direction, he said he was not sure but that it seemed very near and proposed returning at once. As they turned a point of land that had hidden the village, they saw that the woods about were all on fire and made haste back to see how they could help. After landing, they went into the woods and found that all the people had turned out to fight the fire, some with rakes and some with branches of green pine. The green pine serves admirably to whip a fire out.

In some places the villagers would burn a broad belt all around their fences and houses and put the flames out as soon as they had burned a place wide enough to make sure that the fire could not cross it. In other places they sacked away leaves, dead pine straws and grass, leaving no food for the fire. No damage had been done, but some of the ladies who were unused to such scenes were frightened as the long column of fire marched steadily onward, crackling and soaring and leaving blackness and ashes behind. Where there were lightwood trees, the flames caught them and raced from bottom to top in a few minutes, turning them into great pillars of fire. Most of the trees in the immediate vicinity of the village had been cut down, so that within a few hours the fire was out in their neighborhood, except stumps of trees and half rotten logs that flamed and smoked for several days.

Either hunters or stock owners set the woods on fire every spring. The stock owners say it clears the ground of rubbish and lets new grass through quicker, enabling them to herd and pen their cattle earlier. But it must retard the fertilizing of the land, since all the dead vegetation would decay and enrich the earth. Despite various opinions on the practice and the fact that there are laws against it, it is still done.

George now began to think that if he wanted to do much hunting, he had better take Mr. Hunter's offer. So, at the first opportunity, he sent word to Mr. Hunter that he would visit whenever he could come for him. Meanwhile, he made his preparations. He bought some red flannel shirts and coarse clothing that could withstand the saw-like edges of the scrub-palmetto, as well as such ammunition as he thought he might need, and borrowed David's violin. Although now ready and anxious to go, for several days he heard nothing from Mr. Hunter.

One morning David suggested going down the river several miles to the swamp and, as it was unusually dry, seeing if, by walking about, they could come on a deer or some turkeys. Several deer had been killed there, so they decided to try it. They rowed two miles down the river and then landed in an area where the swamp was quite dry in some places but ankle deep in mud in others. Walking slowly just within sight of each other among the cabbage palmettos and the cypress, gum, and bay trees, they kept a good look out for anything that might get up suddenly. They saw fresh tracks of both deer and turkey but reached the hammock without having seen anything. The swamp extended along the river and was about a mile wide. Behind it began the hammock, which was dry and elevated some feet above the swamp. They walked half a mile along the edge of the hammock and then took what they thought was a direct line for their boat, coming out, much to their pleasure, precisely where it lay. But though they had seen plenty of deer and turkey signs, they saw nothing to shoot. They were, however, satisfied, knowing they could go swamp hunting without dogs.

When George reached the house, he found that Mr. Hunter had been waiting several hours for him. He had been prevented by a family illness from coming before. George was very glad to see him, and they set out in the buggy for Mr. Hunter's, reaching the house about dark. That evening George played his violin for the family's amusement. Before going to bed, Mr. Hunter said that they would start early in the morning and drive to Spring Branch Bay, where they had run the deer on their former hunt. He said he would take Dragon and Ruler and go over and get Mr. Bliss, their next door neighbor, to join him with his dogs. When he set out from Mr. Bliss's house, he would blow his horn to let George and his younger son John know that they should leave. James, the older boy, had been sick and was not strong enough to go. Since John had no shotgun, he took the old rifle, which carried a very large ball but was an excellent weapon. He had never killed a deer, but he had shot a great deal of small game and was used to guns.

CHAPTER VII

A DEER HUNT — A SPLENDID CHANCE — A QUESTION OF HONOR — JOHN KILLS THE DEER — GETS THE BLOODY MARK — LOG ROLLING — NEW QUARTERS — STORY OF THE BIG PANTHERS — A HUNT — A BAD SHOT — THE BIG FIELD — FISHING — A TENACIOUS SQUIRREL

At daybreak the next morning, George was up and soon had his gun loaded and was ready to start. Mr. Hunter was also ready and, taking the dogs, blew his horn cheerfully and set out one way while George and John went another. They walked a half mile through the pine woods and there descended a little hill to a track that crossed the bay in a relatively open place with only a scattering of pine trees. Crossing the flat, they took a station by the top of a fallen lightwood tree just on the slope of the hill. Only a few minutes later they heard a dog opening slowly as if he were trailing a deer. They knew it could not be one of their dogs and sat listening to him for half an hour, at last beginning to wonder at not hearing the horn.

While they were talking, John suddenly exclaimed, "Oh, look! Look at the deer there! Run, George, and get down the hill and I will stay here." George caught a glimpse of two deer moving and, stooping, ran rapidly down the hill under the cover of some bushes toward which the deer were moving. Waiting a moment and finding they did not come, he crawled to the foot of a large solitary live oak surrounded by bushes. He knew the deer must have stopped or else changed their course. Peering through the bushes, he saw a large buck and a doe standing still and looking toward him. But they were nearly a hundred yards off and he knew his gun was not likely to kill at that distance. Since there were no bushes or other cover behind which to crawl closer to the deer, if he were to shoot, he must do it from where he was.

He turned to beckon to John to bring his rifle and found him at his side. John offered him the rifle, but George looked at the deer—his long wished for opportunity—and then at John and thought it a little mean to deprive the young boy of his chance, so nobly told him to shoot. There was no time for talk, since the dog trailing after the deer would probably start them in a few seconds. John moved a little to one side where it was more open and, rising up behind a pine tree, steadied his rifle against it. He aimed carefully for a moment and fired. As the doe dropped behind the palmettos, the buck started and sailed off in splendid style. Thinking the deer might not be mortally wounded, George hurried toward it. But it lay on the ground kicking its last. The ball had entered just behind the fore shoulder in the best spot possible for a kill. George and John were delighted. George caught hold of its hind legs to feel its weight, when the doe drew them up and straightened them out again with such force as very nearly to throw him down.

George then bled the deer and presently they heard Mr. Hunter's horn not far off, blowing steadily. The boys hallooed and, after a time, he came in sight. In his delight, George threw his cap into the air. Then Mr. Hunter moved briskly toward them and Dragon rushed up, smelled the deer and began to wag his tail and snuff the tracks.

"Well, I declare, boys, what good luck," said Mr. Hunter as he came in sight of the deer. "I have been blowing for you this long time. Mr. Bliss could not go, so I gave up the hunt till tomorrow. But everything is all right now, I see. Do you know there was another deer?"

"Oh, yes," said George, "an old buck ran right off toward where you were."

"I was walking carelessly along, wondering why you did not come, when I heard the rifle and supposed you had fired at a squirrel, thinking the hunt given up. A minute or so afterward, I heard a clipping in the palmetto behind me and twirled around. I brought my gun up to my face, but I was too late and just caught a glimpse of the buck as he disappeared over the brow of the hill. And before I could get a sight of him again, he was out of shot. Well, John, that was a first rate shot. But why did you not shoot the buck?"

"Because the buck was standing with its breast toward me while the doe presented its broadside looking over its shoulder at me," said John.

"That was right then," said his father.

Mr. Hunter now began preparing the deer so that he could carry it. He cut it open, took out its entrails, cut off its head, and skinned each leg. He then tied the skins of the left hind leg and the right fore leg together and the other two in the same manner, so it was ready to carry. "Now here is something singular," said Mr. Hunter to George. George came up to see what he meant, and John came too. Mr. Hunter dipped one hand in the deer's blood and, before John knew what was coming, caught him with the other and rubbed the blood over his face. John struggled and kicked, but it was in vain until his father let go of him. Then he ran and his father made as if he would catch him again, simply for the fun of seeing him run. Mr. Hunter and George screamed and laughed at his ludicrous appearance and efforts to escape.

"Ha! Ha!" said Mr. Hunter. "You forgot to ask for the cross, did you?"

It was over now and John laughed too, thinking how in the excitement of the moment he had forgotten and given his father every chance to play with him.

"Keep it on." said George. "Go on ahead and see what they say at home when they see you with a bloody face."

"I will," said John, "but I am afraid mother will think something has happened to me when she first sees me."

"As she would," said Mr. Hunter. "She has seen such things before."

Mr. Hunter now picked up the deer and, running his arms through the loops, jerked it on his back, carrying it as easily as if it were a lamb. John went home first and found his mother looking out the door for them. When she saw him at a distance, she did not know what was the matter. But as soon as she saw that he was laughing, she knew what had happened and laughed too, calling James to come and see his brother.

Although Mr. Hunter was sorry that George had not killed the deer, he could not but admire the young man's conduct in refusing to take the rifle from John. "Never mind," he said to George, "your turn will come. If I could only spare the time, I would hunt with you every day till you killed one. Oh! how I want you to kill that first deer so I can put the mark on you." George shook his head and laughed, thinking that he would play a trick in return.

That afternoon Mr. Hunter went to Mr. Bliss's for a log rolling, and George went along to watch. In clearing Florida pine land, the settlers do not cut down the trees but merely girdle them and plant their first crop of cotton among the green trees. That first planting generally yields a half crop. The next year, the trees are dead and the settlers get a whole crop, with the trees no more in the way than stumps would be. After two or three years, the dead trees begin falling. Then just before spring ploughing, the settlers cut the trees into easily handled lengths and call on their neighbors for a log rolling.

Log rolling simply means carrying or rolling the cut trees into piles so they will burn readily. The trees, dry and dead, burn fiercely, so the settlers gradually get rid of them. Fields with these dead pines look dreary to eyes accustomed to the trim fields of long settled districts. All the neighbors generally attend log rollings because everyone will eventually need the same help. Sometimes thickly settled districts have them every day for weeks. While some of these affairs are merely excuses for regular jollification, the settlers generally do a great amount of hard and laborious work in a short time. At Mr. Bliss's, George met most of the people from that vicinity and enjoyed eating supper with them.

The next day was Sunday. Since a religious service was only held once a month, George spent the day reading, walking about, and talking with Mr. Hunter. Although they intended to hunt Monday morning, it proved rainy, so Mr. Hunter helped him fit up the cotton-house for his headquarters.

Mr. Hunter had just moved into his home and had not had time to put things in order or to build all the accommodations he needed. The former owner had built a storehouse for his cotton during the picking season, and it was now empty. George thought he would prefer sleeping there to sleeping in the house because he would have a better opportunity to be alone for reading or other purposes.

So that morning they cleared up the house, made of pine boards nailed on a frame. There were cracks between the edges of all the boards but the roof was tight, which was all that was needed in an East Florida house. Mr. Hunter made a bedstead, a table and a bookshelf. Then George got his trunk, took out his books and used nails to hang his clothes and gear on. This done, John and he cut stakes and drove them all around the house to prevent the pigs from going under it.

Settlers built all their houses in the country on short poles, raising them three or four feet from the ground to allow air to circulate and discourage insects. Most country families keep a drove of hogs, with their owners' mark notched in their ears and then turned out to get their own living. They are long legged, long nosed, thin, slab-sided animals, but they increase very fast and are excellent eating, especially when they are "kept up" a short time, which means fattened before being killed.

George felt highly pleased with his new quarters, in fact more so that he had ever been in even the most beautifully furnished room. For there was something so novel about living in the woods, lying in bed, looking out among the pine trees and listening to the wind singing in their tops that it just pleased his fancy. John agreed to share his bed, since he preferred having someone with him at night. At first George was almost afraid to go out to his house on dark nights, but he soon became accustomed to it. He would generally build a small fire near the door and sit talking with the boys for hours. They told him of the strange things they had seen in the wild woods, and he told them in return of the wonderful things in the great cities, which they had never seen.

Mr. Hunter had told George that he could not go hunting every day because he had not the time to spare, but he proposed going for an hour or so before breakfast and making a short drive almost any day. The next morning they started to drive to Spring Branch Bay again. Mr. Bliss and Mr. Hunter set out on their horses to put the dogs in at one end, while George and John took post—one at the tree top and the other near the large live oak. After a time, they heard the dogs at a distance and in a few minutes George saw Mr. Hunter riding quickly for a stand near him. Mr. Hunter took his stand, tied his horse in the bushes nearby, and called to George to look out, as the dogs kept coming closer and closer. From his actions, George, assuming that he had seen a deer, looked intently to the spot where he expected it to appear. He heard a noise in some nearby bushes and, in an instant, brought his gun down. But a great hog ran out of the bushes, so George raised his gun. The dogs now seemed bothered and ran round and round in a thick part of the bay, not far off. They stayed so long that Mr. Hunter said it was a catamount that they were after. He tried to get to them but found the bay so wet that he gave it up and called off the dogs.

"Well, this too bad," said he to George as he came up. "We teach our dogs to hunt foxes and catamounts whenever they find them, since we want to kill off all the varmints here. But it is not so pleasant to have them hunt catamounts when you want deer. Well, it is so late now that we must give it up and try again some other time."

That evening George asked Mr. Hunter what he meant by a catamount. Mr. Hunter replied that they generally called a wild cat a catamount. "But," he added, "it is possible that the dogs were after a panther or, as some call them, a tiger, this morning."

"Why," said George, "I did not know that there were panthers about here."

"It is not often that they are seen here, but over in Marion County, where I formerly lived, I shot a great many and among them the largest two that had ever been seen there."

"Oh! Tell me all about it! A Panther Hunt! That is just what I want to hear about."

"Well, I will try to tell you. But I am a poor hand at telling stories.

"It was when I was living across the river in Marion County, as I said before. I had been sick for several weeks, but feeling better one morning, I thought I would go out on a hunt. I took my two dogs, Sam and Raymond. Sam was the one I had in the bear fight that I told you about, but Raymond was better than Sam. He was the best dog for all kinds of game and varmint that I ever saw. I could have swapped him for a good horse any day. I had walked about two miles from the house when I saw a great many buzzards in a shuck near the end of the prairie. Thinking it likely they were drawn by something that had been killed by varmints, I started to go and see what it was. The dogs ran off that way, ahead of me. And when they got there, I heard them scream out and knew they had found some kind of varmint there.

"They ran through a very thick scrub. After about fifteen minutes, I heard them start baying and knew they had treed whatever it was what they were after. I started and ran for them, though I was quite weak and feeble, but I knew the varmint might leave again and so I did my best. When I came up, I found them baying at the foot of a leaning tree. I looked up it but soon saw there was nothing there. If it had been any other dog but Raymond, I should have thought the varmint had fooled him, for I knew their trick of running up one tree and jumping from that to the next and so on for a distance and then descending and running off. But Raymond couldn't be fooled that way. After barking awhile at the tree which the animal went up, if he did not see it, he would strike a large circle. And then if he found no other trail, he would come back and bay fiercer than ever. Well, as both dogs were there and seemed so sure about it, I began looking into the trees around the leaning one. Sure enough, in a pine tree thirty or forty yards beyond, and about forty feet from the ground, I saw a large panther standing with its hind legs on a limb close to the trunk of the tree, while his body was hidden by it. His head showed on the other side and looked down on me with his fierce eyes rolling in an awful savage way.

"But I had my trusty rifle—Danger—with me and I had risked my life on her often, for I had put myself in places where I knew if she did not deal death it was death to me. I never feared anything when I had her in my hand. I first thought I would shoot it in the breast and raised my rifle. Since that might not kill it instantly, it might have life enough left to cripple one of my dogs. So I took a dead aim right between its eyes and fired. At the crack of the rifle, it fell backwards, crashing through the limbs below, down into the scrub. At the same moment, I heard a tremendous thrashing in a scrub oak not more than twenty feet high that stood right behind and partly over me. I turned my head and saw another panther, the biggest one I ever saw, right in the air as it sprang from the oak. Its feet were stretched out and its head and tail up in the air. And when it struck the ground, it fairly bounced and dashed off through the scrub.

"My dogs had gone to the one I had shot, and I could not get them away from it and on the track of the other one before it had had time to run a half mile. After I did get them on its track, they ran away, out of hearing, so that if they ever treed it or not I didn't know. I found I had shot the first one right where I wanted to; I could not have put the ball more plumb with my thumb and finger. I have killed a great many and that was the largest she-panther I ever saw. I would like to have taken her home, but I was too weak. So I put it where I could find it again and, hearing nothing from the dogs, went home. Afterwards, I went back and got some of its teeth and claws.

"I was very glad that I had killed this one, because I was satisfied that the pair were the ones that had done so much mischief by killing my hogs and my neighbor's. We had often seen their tracks, and I don't doubt they had killed a hundred of our hogs. After I had killed it, its male was more mischievous than ever, rambling regularly about the country. I often saw its tracks across the newly ploughed ground and I think it did more mischief in a month than both had done in two.

"I had killed the first one in February. The following July one of my neighbors and myself were returning from a deer hunt. We had a deer in a cart and were coming through a thick hammock, when my dogs started something which I knew must be a varmint. I told my neighbor that it was a varmint and that he had better get ready. He jumped out of the cart, tied his horse, and then ran around the outside of the hammock. I kept in the road. The dogs had been dodging about only five minutes when I saw the varmint coming right toward me from under the limbs of a fallen live oak. I had my double barreled shotgun, Rattlesnake. It was large gun and had thirteen blue whistlers in each barrel. As soon as he was clear of the limbs, I fired at his left shoulder and he came down all in a heap, then floundered along and struggled to within five steps of me and then lay still for a minute as if dead.

"One of my young pups ran up to the back of the panther's head as it lay on its side. It fetched a tremendous lick at him with one of its paws backward over its head, as savage and sensible as if it had never been hurt at all. The puppy dodged down and it just missed him. I saw that the panther had life enough left to kill my dogs when they came up, so I put my gun to its breast and fired into him the other charge, which settled him at once. I saw that this was the mate to the one I had killed before. My friend now came up and we made several attempts before we could get the animal in the cart, it was so heavy. Old hunters who were among the first settlers and others who saw it said it was the largest panther they had ever seen. Its tail was short, having been partly cut off in some trap. I kept its claws and teeth for a long while, but have given them all away."

The next morning Mr. Hunter and George went to try for a deer before breakfast at a small bay close to the house, which George had named the Notch Bay. Mr. Hunter put George at a stand in a deep notch in the bay, across which the deer generally ran. Then Mr. Hunter took the dogs and went on the other side of the bay and put them in. In a few minutes George heard Dragon trailing about and in a short time knew from his quick eager cries that he had jumped a deer. George was on the lookout; and, sure enough, as he watched, a small deer sneaked out of the bay and ran along the edge of and mostly behind the palmetto, which was very high. As he fired at it, it bounded into the bay, quick as a flash. The dogs did not come for some time, since they were trailing another deer. Finally, Mr. Hunter came and asked where the deer was.

George had to acknowledge that it had run away. "Where were you when you fired and where was the deer?" asked Mr. Hunter.

George showed him as nearly as he could. "Why, George, you ought to have shot him right down," said Mr. Hunter. "That was a bad miss." George had to agree but said the deer was a small one and so low down behind the palmettos that he only saw the top of its back.

"Oh!" said Mr. Hunter. "It was a yearling and the dogs were on the trail of the doe. They ran them out of here a few weeks ago as I was passing in a cart. Well, your shot was about the right height. See here where it cut the palmettos. You must have shot either before or behind it. Here are its tracks; see where it jumped after you fired. But there is no blood here."

Mr. Hunter tried to follow the yearling's tracks, but the bay was so wet that he could only go a few yards into it. When the dogs came back, he put them on the trail. They ran off a long way and came back again, showing that the deer had not been hurt much.

"Well, let us go up to breakfast," said Mr. Hunter. "Now, the next time you get a shot at a deer, don't be in a hurry. Stop and think."

"Now I am going to take good aim and kill that deer."

"If you do that, I'll guarantee you the deer. That yearling would have been tender eating, if you had got him."

"Well," said George laughing, "I guess I gave him a terrible fright at any rate."

Mr. Hunter had only thirty acres of ground deadened and fenced and wanted twenty acres more. Since it was too late in the season to clear it, he adopted the plan of a number of newcomers in that neighborhood and hired what he wanted. The land that he and the others hired was situated in what was called the big field, about three hundred acres which had been cleared by a man who had a large number of negroes. When he died, his negroes were distributed among his heirs and the land sold. The present owner had not enough men to cultivate it and was glad to hire to the neighbors all they wished. The field had mostly excellent land and most of the trees had already fallen and been burned, so there was not much log rolling to be done. It was on the shore of Dunn's Lake and had a long pond in the rear, so that the people using it had only a little fence to build and repair, an important item in country where cattle and hogs roam at large.

Dunn's Lake stretched out fourteen miles long and about five miles wide. A part of the field, fifty feet above the level of the lake, commanded an extensive view over it. On this ridge, the men who hired land built three or four bark camps to spare themselves the trouble of going home every night while working in the field. They brought provisions for themselves and their horses, bedding and necessary cooking utensils. Pine bark shelters were all that men, used to sleeping in open log houses, wanted in a climate like Florida's.

As Mr. Hunter was going over to the field that day, he told George to get into the cart and bring his trolling line. He suggested that they get a boat and catch some fish in the lake. George did so. The field was about two miles off and the road wound past a number of ponds of clear water. On the way, the dogs treed several fox squirrels, and Mr. Hunter waited for George to shoot them. George had never seen so large a field before. He was quite pleased with the view from it, the first view from a hill that he had had in the state. After looking for a time, he asked Mr. Hunter if anyone lived on the eastern shore. Mr. Hunter replied that it was uninhabited from there to the coast, with only vast pine woods and probably very poor land.

"There must be good hunting there," said George.

"I suppose there is," said Mr. Hunter, "and if we had a good boat, we could get up a party and go over there to camp and hunt. But we have no good boat."

In the afternoon Mr. Hunter and George went down to the lake and took a canoe, with Mr. Hunter paddling while George trolled. They had very good luck; George caught nine trout, one of them a twelve pounder, the largest he had ever caught. They returned home and at sundown, Jimmy told George he had seen a very large fox squirrel run up a prairie tree near the house. After George got his gun and some shot and Jimmy took the rifle, they walked out to try and shoot it. Mrs. Hunter said there should be enough to make a large squirrel pie. When they got to the tree, they found the squirrel in its top blown about so by the wind, that he would be hard to hit with a rifle. George fired at him six times without bringing him down. The dogs, hearing the firing, had come and were now yelping about the tree.

George suggested that one of the boys go to the house and get an axe, so they could cut down the tree and let the dogs catch the squirrel. John went to the house, but Mr. Hunter came back with him and said there was no use in cutting down the tree. As soon as the squirrel felt it going, he would simply jump to another one. Besides, the dogs might get killed since they would probably run right under the tree. So Mr. Hunter took the rifle, thinking to show George how to do it. But the wind waved the top of the tree about so much that he fired three times before he brought the squirrel down. They picked it up and went home laughing about the squirrel that it took two men, two boys, two dogs and the two guns to capture. Mr. Hunter said that all the shots would make his neighbor Bliss think that Sam Jones, the Indian Chief, was back again.

CHAPTER VIII

GEORGE KILLS A DEER — CUTS A NEW ROAD — FISH-
ING — SHOOT A FOX — VELZ FRIGHTENED BY A BEAR
— A DEER HUNT — TROLLING IN DUNN'S LAKE — AL-
LIGATORS — TURKEY HUNT WOUNDS A DEER — FISH-
ING SPOILED BY ALLIGATORS — ALLIGATOR STORIES

The next day Mr. Hunter and John went to the big field for two days. Jimmy had some work to do, and so George took his gun and the dogs and thought he would try for a deer by himself. He started for Long Bay, where he had his first hunt here. Since he knew the way to the stand called the Buck's Head, which Mr. Pierce had shown him, he thought he would go there if the dogs got a deer up. He whistled and cheered to the dogs as he had seen others do as they ran about in the palmettos and up and down the side of the bay. Soon Dragon opened loudly, dashing into the bay and opening faster. George started running to his stand. It was a full three quarters of a mile that he had to go and he feared the deer might get there first. But Dragon trailed some time in the bay before he jumped it. George was very near his stand when both the dogs began opening steadily. He reached it and took post behind a pine tree fifty yards from the edge of the bay.

He had been there only a minute and the dogs were coming straight towards him in full cry, when he saw a deer slip out of the bay and walk a few paces directly to-ward him. He leveled his gun and then thought of what Mr. Hunter had told him, so he waited an instant. The deer took a few more steps toward him, where it seemed to scent him because it turned toward the edge of the bay. Now, thought George, is my time. With one more jump, the deer passed a mass of saplings blocking the shot and came into full view. George, who had kept his gun leveled on it all the time, fired. The deer disappeared behind a large pine and a clump of high palmettos, so George kept his gun to his face for half a minute to give it the other barrel if it appeared. But it never came from behind the palmettos, where George heard a dull pounding noise like something kicking the sod. He could hardly believe it possible that he had thrown it, but, uncocking the other barrel, he ran around the bushes and found a deer with its haunches resting on the ground, unable to get up on its hind legs. It was jumping with its fore feet, trying to get into the bay. George remembered Mr. Hunter's caution not to go too near a wounded deer and attempt to use a knife when a gun would do better. So he raised his gun and shot it in the head. After it fell over dead, he bled it, and in a few minutes the dogs came up. They bit it once as if to see if it were dead, then licked up the blood and lay down beside it. It was a fine large doe in good condition.

George would have greatly preferred a buck so he could show the horns at home, but he was delighted with this one. I say he was delighted, and so he was. As he knelt down by the deer and examined its beautiful form and its soft mild eye, however, he felt almost sorry that he had shot it. But he knew animals were made for man's use; and, though he could not say he shot it just because he was hungry, he knew the other deer was almost all eaten. Since he had not yet learned to like bacon or salt pork, he was pleased with the idea of having a savory venison steak of his own killing for dinner. Attempting to lift the deer, he found that half of it was as much as he could manage even though he wanted to take it home whole. And since Mr. Hunter was absent, he was in no danger of being crowned or marked. The idea of killing his first deer when Mr. Hunter was not at home to mark him pleased George. Because he was only half a mile from the house, he blew a horn which Jimmy had made for him, hoping that Jimmy would hear it and come to him. When he did not come, George walked up to the house and saw Mrs. Hunter standing by the door.

"Where is Jimmy?" asked he.

"In the house," answered Mrs. Hunter.

"I want him to help me bring up a deer."

"Have you killed a deer?" exclaimed Mrs. Hunter and Jimmy together. And Jimmy was out in a minute. They were all glad that George had gotten one after so much diligence and disappointment.

"I am more pleased," said Mrs. Hunter, "than if Mr. Hunter had shot a dozen deer."

"I will leave my gun and we will get a nice pole to carry the deer on," said George.

So they got a pole about ten feet long and then went back for the deer. They skinned the bottoms of the legs and then put the pole through the sinews. Getting the pole under it, they walked a short distance with the pole resting on their shoulders.

"It is of no use," said George. "It would take us half a day to get it to the house. So let us cut off its head and open it."

"Yes," replied Jimmy. "You don't want these parts near the house any way. Leave them for the buzzard's share."

So they cut off its head and opened its body. Jimmy called it one of the fattest, prettiest deer he had ever seen, and he had seen hundreds. By putting their coats under the ends of the pole to protect their shoulders and by stopping frequently, they finally reached the house . George then passed a stick through the sinews of its hind legs, hung it up and spent the rest of the morning skinning and carving it up. He took great pains to keep the skin nice so he could preserve it and nailed it to the end of the corn house to dry.

The next morning George set out for the big field, taking some venison with him for Mr. Hunter. When he reached the field, he went out to where Mr. Hunter and John were at work and said, "I came over to bring you some venison."

"What? Venison! Have you shot a deer or are you humbugging? Let me see. Well, I declare! John, this is venison. Well, I am glad of it. I am right glad that you have done it at last. Now you will have better success in hunting, for you will be less anxious and consequently shoot better." George then told them all about it. Though shooting deer had been a common occurrence for Mr. Hunter, he listened with as much interest as if George had shot a panther instead of a deer.

George had to do his deer hunting in the morning while the trails were fresh, for the dogs could not follow them after the sun had shone upon them. With nothing to do in the afternoon but fish and write letters, sometimes he would go out after squirrels. But he could generally hunt them better in the morning too. The road leading to Mr. Hunter's house was very crooked, as it wound about among the trees; and George had heard Mr. Hunter say that some day he meant to lay out a straight one from his door to the main road. After looking at the proposed route, George thought that he and the boys could open the road. One afternoon he discussed it with John, who agreed, so they took two axes and set out. George laid a new path out carefully to avoid cutting down any large trees and, at the same time, have it straight. When he found that only three small trees needed clearing, they cut them down and removed them. After that, they had to move a great many limbs and pieces of fallen trees, but finally they got it clear a quarter of a mile, to the pond's end, where their road crossed the old one.

The only obstacle remaining was a very large lightwood tree lying directly across the road. It was nearly three feet in diameter and so hard that their axes made very little impression on it. The next day George suggested burning instead of cutting it. So they piled chips and wood about it and set it on fire, constantly replenishing the flames. By night they had a passage wide enough for the road. Then they felled a tree directly across each end of the old road where the new one crossed it to oblige travelers to take the new road, since the horses had become accustomed to the old one and would probably not turn into the new one. When Mr. Hunter came home, he was surprised to find the road blocked up. But seeing the blazes on the trees and the open road, he understood at once what had happened and was much pleased.

A few days later the boys continued their road on to the main road. Removing all the fallen trees and lightwood snags took several days. They found too that they could not run it exactly straight without felling some large pine trees, which would have been too laborious for them. When they were finished, George was delighted with the view up this long aisle in the forest. Sitting in the doorway of the house, they could see a person coming for half a mile. The pine trees are so thick in this area that one can see only a very short distance into the woods. Before their new road, the first intimation that anyone was coming was their appearance at the door.

One afternoon Mr. Hunter proposed going over to the lake to fish. So he, George and the two boys set out, taking Nelly, Mr. Hunter's mare, with them. On the way, they stopped at the edge of a bay to cut some fishing poles. While they did so, Dragon ran into the bay and began trailing. When he had reached the end, the dog passed out into a scrub in full cry but soon turned and came directly back again when a large fox jumped out of the bushes near George. He raised his gun but the first barrel snagged. He then tried the second one, and saw Reynard roll over. But the fox jumped up again and raced toward the other end of the bay, where Mr. Hunter stopped him with a charge of buck shot.

At the lake they bailed the boat out and Mr. Hunter tied Nelly to a young tree at the boat landing, which was in a hammock on the lake's edge. Pushing off, they rowed down to a cove where they wanted to fish. But the lake was very rough and soon a shower came up, forcing them to row ashore and take shelter under some cypress trees. Since the trees were covered with moss, they protected everyone well. When the shower passed, the wind died down and the fish began to bite. They fished for only short time, since it was sunset, but caught as many as they wanted—trout, bream, and several large blue cat fish. When they arrived at the boat landing, they were surprised to find Nelly gone. She had torn up the young tree by the roots, evidently after a hard struggle, and left her saddle a little way off. Following her tracks, they found she had taken the trail for home. In a deserted field half way home they found her grazing. She was very frightened and resisted all Mr. Hunter's efforts to make her go back to the lake for the saddle, so he turned toward home.

"What do you suppose frightened her?" asked George.

"It must have been a bear," replied Mr. Hunter, "for if you notice her now, you will see how she avoids every black stump. I shall go down after the saddle in the morning and see if I can find any bear signs there."

"Is it time for the bears to come out yet?"

"A few get out as early as this, though most of them wait until April. They leave sign enough when they come, as it is easy to see where they have been at work pulling the palmetto buds which constitute a part of their food."

The next morning Mr. Hunter went down to the boat landing but had great difficulty in urging Nelly to go into the hammock to get his saddle. Though he saw no sign, he was satisfied that a bear had frightened the horse.

Since George had promised to keep his diary and had kept a very exact one, we think we cannot do better than to give some extracts from it.

*   *   *   *   *   *   *   *   *   *   *

Thursday—I helped Mr. Hunter pull down a line of fence, and after he had carted it across the field, to build it up again. This is one great advantage of the "worm fences" that they have here. They can easily be moved when one wishes to take more land into his field. In the afternoon I practiced firing at a barrel head, which I got John to roll on the ground. I was successful in hitting it with part of my load every time. This, I think is good practice for deer hunting.

Friday—Jimmy and I went to drive the notch bay. I took the dogs, put them in, and told Jimmy to go to the lower end of the bay and take a stand. I drove down the bay without starting anything until I came to the lower end. There the dogs came suddenly on two deer. They jumped up within fair shot of me, and I raised my gun, when I thought that I might shoot Jimmy whom I had told to go to the end of the bay, and who was probably near, and just in a range. So I lowered my gun, and the deer ran across toward where I had told Jimmy to go. I kept listening, each instant expecting to hear his gun: but I did not hear it, and saw the deer run across the open pine woods, with the dogs close behind them. I felt very much vexed, as I had had such a splendid chance, but had not fired on Jimmy's account. I crossed the bay to see where he was, and found he had just reached the end of the bay. He said he had walked slowly as he did not feel well, and had got there in time to see the deer, but not to shoot them. I still felt vexed, but was satisfied I had done right in not firing toward where I had told him to go.

Saturday—I took my rifle and spinner and went to the big field; on the way I shot two fox squirrels. Found Mr. Hunter engaged in plowing while the boys were pulling up the last year's cotton stalks and burning them in piles. The field was an interesting sight, as there were so many different parties of men at work in it. There were about thirty horses, and forty men at work in various parts of the field. I went down to the Lake, got the little canoe, and went out to troll. The canoe is so small that I was obliged to sit-in the bottom of it. I worked a paddle with my hands, and held the line in my teeth. There is a dense growth of trees along the shore, then a wide stretch of rushes among which were many alligators and ducks. I paddled close along the edge of the rushes, and in an hour caught five trout. The alligators that were lying along the banks of the river, seeing me, would come tearing out through the rushes into the deep water just before me, and then sink. Whether it was with fright or a desire to see what was coming I do not know, but I disliked their being so close to me while I was in such a frail boat, the least movement to one side of which, would have capsized it. Some of my fish were so active that I was obliged to run a paddle handle through their gills, to keep them from jumping over the low sides of the boat. While I was paddling toward the boat landing an enormous alligator came splashing out through the rushes into the deep water, not far before me. He saw me but did not seem at all afraid, and waited until I was within fifty feet of him. I was a little frightened, but thought the best way was to put a bold face on the matter; so I gave a whoop and dashed my canoe toward him when he sank; and I paddled hard for the landing. The alligator rose after I had passed, and did not appear to care much for me. I went up to the camp in the field, and we cooked some of the fish for dinner. Mr. Hunter told me he had killed a turkey in the morning, and said that down in the south end of the field, where it was partly grown over with low bushes, a drove of turkeys had been seen for several days in succession. He thought if I went there and hunted about I might get a shot at some of them. I took the rifle and started, but finding Dragon was following me drove him back. When I got into the bushes and sat down to listen, Dragon came to me again. I beat him and drove him off, but it was of no use; he would not lose sight of me, and the moment he saw me take my gun, he was up close to me again. I feared he would drive the turkeys away before I could get a shot at them. I crossed the fence of the field, and went into a thick wood. It was on the slope of the Lake side, and after walking about, I came to a stream and a little fall. I was delighted to see something that reminded me of the woods at the North. I sat down by the fall, drank and enjoyed the music of it. While I was there two oxen came through the woods to drink at the stream. They came down to the water near me, but kept snuffing the air as if it were not right. I suppose they scented me. After a time I arose quickly to my feet, and the instant they saw me, they wheeled and went through the woods like a small tornado.

It was of no use to hunt for turkeys there after that; so I went back to the fence near the Lake and sat down. I had been there but a short time, when I thought I heard the yelping of turkeys in the field. I crossed the fence and after tearing my way through the briars, I came out into an old road, and sat down on a log. The road led to an old wharf which I could see, as I was near the water. Dragon who had followed me, now seemed to scent something, and dashed into the bushes near me, when up flew a large gobbler and flew directly over my head. I raised the rifle, but thought I could not hit him, so did not fire. If I had had my shotgun I could have dropped him. I then got hold of Dragon and held him, thinking there must be other turkeys about, and they might attempt to cross the road. In a few minutes I heard them calling, and if I had known how to imitate their call I could have killed a number. I did not though, and had to sit still in hopes to get a shot. They kept coming nearer and nearer, and at last I saw one coming out of the bushes on the road. I let go of Dragon and picked up my rifle, slowly and cautiously at first, but as soon as Dragon saw me take it, he dashed off towards the turkey, and I had to move so quickly that I fired without half a sight, and a whole drove flew up and off into the woods. I was so vexed with the dog that I tried to get hold of him, to give him what Mr. Hunter called a "frailing," but he kept out of my reach. If I had known enough, I might have made good use of him, and had him run them up suddenly when they often alight on the nearest tree, and give you a fair shot, but these all flew into the swamp. I then started for the camp as it was sunset. I found Mr. Hunter somewhat alarmed, at my staying so late; he had heard my gun, and was afraid I had shot myself. I did not reach home until dark.

Sunday—I read, walked and conversed with Mr. Hunter.

Monday—I completed some letters, and started to take them to a neighbor who was going to Welaka. On the way Dragon got on trail of a deer, and followed it into the Long bay. I ran for the stand where I had shot the deer before. When I got there I remembered that my gun was only loaded with fine shot. I had a few turkey shot in my pocket, and was trying to draw the loads when I found I should not have time. I only had time to run down a few of them on top of the fine shot, when I saw the deer jump out of the bushes, and run within thirty yards of me, but behind some bushes. I stepped one side took a deliberate aim, and fired a barrel intending to fire the other the next instant, but did not get an opportunity, for the deer jumped about for a minute, as if he were crazy, and then dashed off into the bay. Dragon came out and followed his trail in again. He went but a short distance, when he stopped crying, and stayed in the bay two hours. I was satisfied that he had the deer, and tried several times to go in after it. But it was the wettest thickest part of the bay, and I was obliged to give it up. I was confident the deer was there, and hoped Mr. Hunter would come home from the field that night, so that he could go after it in the morning. But as he did not, I suppose the buzzards got him. Received letter from home, and one from Uncle James. They are all well.

Tuesday—Mr. Hunter had told me it was "gobbling time" with the wild turkeys, and that if I would get up, and be at the side of the Lake in the hammock near the big field, by day break, I could probably hear some of the turkeys gobbling; and by using great care I might get under the tree they were on, and as soon as it became high-enough to see the sights of my gun, I could shoot them. This is the way in which he generally hunts them. John came home last night, and we arranged it to go before daybreak, and try for some turkeys. I got up at three o'clock and looked out. It was not as clear and quiet as I should have liked, as Mr. Hunter says they gobble only on clear warm mornings. But I thought we would try; so awoke John, and we dressed leisurely and set out. It was still quite dark and we had two miles to go. Several times we got off of the road, as we could almost see nothing to guide us. The only way we got back, was by feeling with our feet, for the cart tracks, which were not very deep. It seemed very strange to me, to be tramping through the dark pine woods, at night, with a gun on my shoulder. Occasionally the thought would cross my mind, what would I do if we were to meet a bear? But I am beginning to feel at home in the woods, and do not think I should have much fear of anything, as long as I had a loaded gun in my hands.

When we reached the side of a pond, we saw the morning star just rising over the tree tops, on the opposite side of it. We pushed on and reached the corner of the big field. There we separated. John went into the field down by the side of the Lake, where some had lately been known to roost; and I went into a hammock that been partly cleared. It was very dark when I got under the shadows of the big trees, but I pushed on toward the Lake and sat down not far from, it on a log. I had been there but a short time and it began to get a little lighter, when I heard a turkey in the direction of John, and a moment after one answered him not far from me, and in some trees near the Lake. I worked my way cautiously toward the tree, examining all the tree tops that I could see, and at last saw some dark looking objects on the limb of a tree, nearer than the one I was moving toward. I crawled under it, and got a place where I could take a good sight of them, but I was puzzled. It seemed to me that they were not large enough, or hardly the proper shape. I strained my eyes toward them, looking as intently as I possibly could, but it was impossible for me to decide whether they were turkeys or turkey buzzards, as they were so mixed up with the foliage. I waited until it was light enough to make it impossible for me to move further with any chance of success if I remained there any longer; and then came to the conclusion that they were not wild turkeys, and moved on toward the tree whence I had several times heard one gobble. I got under the tree, but it was thickly covered with moss and leaves. It was a magnolia–grandiflora, and after looking my best, I could discover no turkey. I then made up my mind to wait and shoot him when he flew down. So I sat down in good sight of an open place where I thought he would alight. It was now daylight and I heard a movement in the top of the tree. I was every minute expecting to see the turkey come down, when I heard John shouting and whistling, evidently in search of and coming toward me. There, I thought my luck again! and John came shouting along, until I heard the turkey give a cry of "quit", and away it went over the tree tops, before I could get my gun to my face.

"There," said I as I stepped out from behind the bushes, "you see you have spoiled a shot for me."

John of course was very sorry, and said that as it had become light, he thought there was no farther use in waiting, and was looking for me. He had heard a turkey and going where he supposed it to be, passed under a small tree on which the turkey was and frightened it away. We went up to the camp, and did not feel very proud of what we had done; so said nothing about it. After breakfasting with Mr. Hunter, I went down to the Lake, and out in the canoe to troll. As I came near the place where the large alligator had come out the last time I was here, I saw him coming again. This time he *swam after* me for some distance, and looked so vicious, that I went ashore at the nearest place without catching any fish. I went up to the camp, and stayed there until the men came to dinner, and then told them of it. Some of them laughed at me, and said there was no danger; but I replied that it was the last time I would go out in that little canoe on the Lake. Mr. Hunter said that the alligators needed killing off there if they were as awry as that.

That night Mr. Hunter went home, and during the evening they were talking about the alligator that "ran George out of the Lake." Mr. Hunter said that some day he would go down to the Lake, and see if he could not "turn up some of those fellows."

"Did you ever have any chase you?" I asked.

"Well, not exactly *chase* me; but I was once out on a deer hunt with some neighbors, and we rounded a deer which took to a small Lake that contained a great many alligators. While he was crossing it, I shot him in the head and killed him, and as he was a noble fellow, and we had had a long chase I was determined to have him. The 'gators' hearing the noise and barking of the dogs, began to come up thick, and some of them started for the deer. But some of the party peppered them with rifle balls, and killed or wounded every one that went near the deer.

"I went to work and made a raft of some logs tied together with grape vines; and though it was a poor thing to venture on the lake with, I started, pushing it with a pole. I had to shoot two of them before I got to the deer, and then I had my hands full, for I had to hold the deer, manage my raft, and keep a look out for the 'gators', who several times seemed determined to charge on me. But those on the shore helped me by shooting some more of them, I reached the shore in safety. I would not do it again though for any deer."

"Do you know of anyone who was ever killed by them?" I asked.

"I have known of several negroes who were killed by them, while swimming rivers. One of my neighbors and his son were one day following an old Indian trail that led through one end of a grass pond, where the water was about a foot deep. The old man was ahead and before he could help himself, an alligator that was lying in the grass made at him, caught him by the thigh and pulled him down. His son tried to shoot and strike the alligator, but could not do so without danger of injuring his father, as they were both struggling; the alligator to get him into the deep water to drown him, and the man to get away. At last his son got a chance, fired and wounded the alligator which made him let go his father, but it was months before the old man could get about again. When he did, he took vengeance of alligators generally, for he took to hunting them. He shot great numbers and made them a little scarce in his neighborhood."

CHAPTER IX

STORY OF THE CROOKED FOOTED BUCK — A DEER HUNT — KILLS A BUCK — ATTENDS PREACHING — GIVES VENISON TO WELAKA — LINWOOD SPRING — RE- TURNS TO DAWNS LAKE — HOG HUNTING — A WED- DING — PENNING CATTLE — A TURKEY HUNT

One evening Mr. Hunter said to George, "One of Mr. Pierce's negroes said he knew where the biggest buck about here is. Several times he started the deer either out of the hammock or at the end of a grass pond near the hammock while hauling logs near the orange grove. He says, 'His horns look like a chair frame.' Well, I think we will have to go down that way tomorrow and see if we can't get a shot at him. Dragon can get him up if he is there."

"I hope I can get a good shot at him," said George. "There is nothing in the hunt- ing line I want so much as to carry home a pair of large buck's horns as trophies. Do you ever save any of the horns? I don't see any about here."

"I have not killed any bucks since I have been here, but over in Marion County I had my gate posts and other places ornamented with some very large ones. I killed the buck that had the heaviest horns that had ever been seen in Marion, but I did not preserve them, as I had enough to do to get the carcass of the deer home, without taking the head and horns. Killing that deer pleased me more than anything I had ever killed before, as he had been hunted for so much by others."

"Tell me all about it, please, for nothing interests me as much as your hunting stories and from them I learned how to do things better than by your telling me."

"Well, it was soon after I came to Florida. The deer were plenty in Marion then and used to feed out in the day time, so that we generally hunted them then. Among the deer was one large buck that had been seen by most every one who hunted, but he was so cunning that no one had been able to shoot him. One of his fore feet had met with an accident, I suppose, for the points of the hoof were twisted outwards so that its track could always be distinguished from others and he was called the crooked foot buck. It was about two years after he had first been seen and talked about that I was on a hunt and found out where old crooked foot's hiding place was. I saw him feeding in company with three other deer on a water prairie that was about a mile wide. There were ridges of dry grass and ponds of water scattered about through it, and in the center was an island that was covered with a dense growth of trees. His island was his hiding place but he fed on the prairie. I was very much pleased at finding him, but it was too late to hunt that day. I stood and watched him a while, and saw him lie down after he had done feeding. He was half a mile from me but I knew him from his large size and the peculiar shape of his horns, which had five snags on one beam and four on the other and they all laid parallel and so close to each other that they looked like a board on each side of his head.

"The next day after I had seen the deer, one of my neighbors who had hunted him most was at my house. I told him that I had found out where old crooked foot lived and that I was going to kill him. He said I ought to give him that chance, as he did not doubt but that he had loaded his rifle a hundred of times and hunted with the determination to kill him. I told him I couldn't do it; and he said he thought he knew the place too and meant to hunt and kill him first. That made me a little uneasy, for fear he might find him, as I wanted to kill him.

"A few days afterward there came up a heavy shower about noon; as soon as it had ceased, knowing it would be an excellent time to find him feeding, I mounted my mare and set out for the prairie. As soon as I reached it, there sure enough was the old deer feeding in company with the three others that had been seen him with before. Now, how I was to get within shot of him was the question, as there was not a tree or bush on the prairie and the grass was only two feet high. There was nothing to hide behind except a few scattering bunches of wild millet. I tied my mare out of sight of the deer and crawled down the hill on my hands and knees into the prairie. Then I had to crawl through the grass which grew out of the water, where it was from six inches to a foot deep, holding my rifle in one hand, and taking advantage of every bunch of wild millet that lay between us. As I got nearer to him, the water was deeper, so that at last I could not crawl but had to walk half bent. Deer when feeding are always on the alert. They put their heads down and feed for a minute. Then you will see their tails give a little shake, and then up come their heads and they look about for a minute. Then their tails shake and down go their heads again. Well, I kept a close watch on him and, when I saw his tail shake, I would stop until he had put his head down again and then I would move on.

"In this way I advanced until I reached the last bunch of millet, which was about one hundred and fifty yards from him, when he seemed to have taken an alarm, for he stopped feeding and stood steadily gazing toward me. I had often killed deer at that distance, but I wanted to be very sure of him, after all my trouble, and would much rather have been closer. But I saw that the water was very deep between us – so deep that no grass grew in it. As it seemed my only chance, I raised steadily up, keeping my rifle leveled on him, and, as I came straight, I fired. At the crack of the rifle he jumped and ran about a hundred yards from me as if he had not been touched and then stopped and looked back at the other deer, who had not run, as if he wished them to follow him. I could hardly believe that I had missed him, but he went off as if I had not touched him. I began to feel very much disappointed and commenced loading my rifle, thinking I would shoot one of the other deer, who were nearer to me than he had been. While I was loading, I kept my eye on him and saw him stagger to one side, then stand erect again for a minute, then stagger the other way and fall. I didn't stop to finish loading, but pushed right through the pond and ran up to him. When I reached him, he was perfectly dead. I had hit him just where I wanted to, right behind the shoulder.

"Well, I can't tell nor do I believe you can imagine how pleased I was that I had killed him. I would have liked to have taken him home whole, but he was too heavy to handle. So I opened him, cut off his head, and then dragged him through the grass and water to the side of the prairie. Then I dragged him up the hill to a grove of trees. I bent down a stout sapling, cut off the top of it, tied the deer's legs together and swung it to the tree. I then backed my mare up to it and by the help of the spring of the sapling and by hard lifting, I got the deer across the mare and tied it fast with my saddle strings. I reached home an hour after dark, thinking I had a great prize. I sent word to the other hunters to come and dine with me off of old crooked foot but none of them came. I told my neighbor where he could find the head and he went and got it, for he would hardly believe me until he had seen it. Well, it was astonishing the difference it made in our going out to hunt after that. No one seemed to care half as much about deer hunting. They used to load their rifles so carefully and say, 'Well, I'm a going to have a hunt of old crooked foot today'; and they would hunt day after day in hopes to kill him. He was the master deer of the country. I have never seen one that was near as large as he was.

"I have often watched them and noticed all their movements. A herd of deer when feeding always have a watch deer. When he breaks off into a run, the others follow without waiting to see what the matter is. The watch deer is generally one of the largest and I need to try and pick him out of the herd."

The next morning was fair for a hunt, and so they set out for the orange grove hammock on the side of the lake about two miles north of the big field. It extended along the lake shore for two miles and was about two miles wide. Behind it was a flat piece of land covered with scrub palmetto with a long grass pond, one end of which was full of bushes. They put the dog in the nearest end of the hammock when they arrived. Because he refused to hunt on horseback, George dismounted from Nelly so Mr. Hunter could mount her. George had said that once he learned to manage his gun well, then he could try to manage a horse and gun at the same time. He had never ridden horseback much up North, though he could drive a team well. To tell the truth, he was a little afraid of Nelly who sometimes cut up some bad pranks.

As the dogs hunted the hammock, Mr. Hunter and George moved along its out-skirts. After jumping nothing there, they came out and trailed up the side of the grass pond. At its farthest end, they struck a cold trail and went a long way down the flat land. Mr. Hunter, apparently puzzled, finally told George that, since there was no cover where the dogs were trailing, he thought the deer must be in some of the bushes around the pond. He would stay there while George went back to the other end, for if the deer was jumped it would probably run down the pond's side. So George started back. But before he got many rods, he heard, first, the dogs yell-ing loudly and, the next minute, both barrels of Mr. Hunter's gun. Looking back, he saw the deer on the opposite side of the pond, running almost parallel to his course and making for a point where the hammock extended out into the pond. Be-cause the deer might turn around the end of the pond and head into the hammock, George hurried forward. As he reached the end of the pond, the deer was directly opposite and had no chance of turning toward George. But some of the Pierce boys, on their way to the orange grove, heard the dogs and gun and saw the deer and George. They ran their horses right in front of the deer, shouting and waving their hats, turning it so that it headed straight down to the hammock near George.

George had a fancy that day to try the rifle. Though he knew it was more difficult to use, he also knew it was sure death if it hit anywhere near the right place. The gun carried a large ball, a Cuban yager. George raised the rifle as soon as the buck was out of range of the boys, took a long careful sight, and fired when it was directly opposite. The deer tumbled and rolled, but jumped up again, plunging into the hammock. In another moment their dogs, joined by a pack following the Pierce boys, rushed in after it. While George was taking aim, he heard Mr. Hunter thundering along behind him, and, as he turned, saw Mr. Hunter dashing up on his horse.

"That was well done, George," he shouted. "You hit him fair and we will get him if he don't get into the lake. But I don't think he can run as far as that. Come on to the orange grove trail and we will follow the dogs."

They had gone but a little piece into the hammock when they heard a great roar among the dogs. "There he is," shouted Mr. Hunter. "They have got him and Dragon is fighting off the other dogs. He will not let one of them come near it, not even Ruler."

They hurried on and soon came to the place where the dogs were fighting. The trail crossed a "hanch" (brook) in the hammock. The hanch was ten feet wide and the banks of it several feet high. Sticking to the trail, the poor buck attempted to leap the hanch but his strength gave way. The marks of his fore feet were visible on the opposite bank, and he had fallen into water about a foot deep. Dragon had jumped in beside it. As the other dogs came up, some of them attempted to bite it. But old Dragon was on his dignity and would allow no other dog to smell a deer that he had jumped and so he pitched on every one that attempted it. A number of them must have taken Dragon on at once, for his ears were badly torn. That would never have happened if a single dog had attacked him, as he was not easily beaten. They drove off the dogs and, with the help of the Pierce boys, pulled the deer onto dry land. He was a noble buck and a four snag one. Though his horns were not so immense as the negro had said, still they were large and his body also. Mr. Hunter opened him, and then they put him across Nelly for the trip home.

Despite firing from a great distance, Mr. Hunter had hit the deer in several places. But the wounds were not severe enough to have stopped him. George had hit a little behind the right place, but on the proper level. When they cut him up, they sent the Pierce boys a quarter for their help. George learned that they were going to Welaka the following Monday and arranged to go with them, because he wanted to take some letters and see some of his friends there. He also wanted to take a saddle of venison to Col. B.

The next day was Sunday. Since there would be preaching in the school house, Mr. Hunter and some of his family brought George. When they arrived, they found a number of vehicles and people already there. Most of the females had come in carts, which better adapted than wagons to the roads through the pine woods, where it is often necessary to make very short turns. The school house, a common log building, stood on one side of the road. About a fourth of it was open to the wind, because the chinks between its logs had not been filled. The females had gone in and taken seats as fast as they came, but the men mostly sat on the ground under trees in front of the door. Mr. Hunter and George talked with those they knew until the preacher came. Then everyone followed him into the school. There were some rough benches and in one corner a substitute for a pulpit which made the preacher look as if he were standing in a high dry goods box. Although he was a tall man, only his head and the tops of his shoulders could be seen.

While the preacher had not much education, he was earnest and sincere and was said to have done much good in that part of the country. A farmer who lived forty miles off, he was obliged to leave home on Saturday morning and did not return until Monday nights. But he did not receive a cent for his labor.

After the services, Mr. Hunter and George went home with Mr. Pierce and took dinner with him. They had bear meat and a number of kinds of fresh vegetables. George remained there all night, and the next morning Mr. Hunter sent over the saddle of venison for George to take to Welaka. They set out in a farm wagon by the upper road, which George had not yet been on, passing a number of clearings and cabins. About four miles from Welaka, they stopped and got out of the wagon to pay Linwood Spring a visit.

This spring boils up in a hammock about one hundred yards from the road. Its basin is about fifteen feet across and its water sulphurous and very clear. A short distance below the spring, the water expands into a little pond, where they saw many fish and turtles. Reaching Col. B's house, George proudly presented his family the saddle of venison from his own killing. He found David well and told him of some of his hunts. They agreed to get up a big hunt when George came back permanently, which he expected to do in a week or so. George remained all night, got his letters and mailed others.

The next afternoon Mr. Hunter sent in a horse for him. When he arrived back, Mrs. Hunter said that Mr. Hunter had gone hog hunting with some of the neighbors. The party returned shortly afterwards with two very large hogs and a buck in the cart. Mr. Hunter told George that if he had been with them, he would have seen lots of fun. Mr. Lyndale, a neighbor, owned two large black hogs that he had not seen in a long time, but which he knew used the hammock by the lakeside. He wanted to get them and fatten them for killing. So with one of sons and Mr. Hunter, he set out, mounted on their horses and accompanied by a number of catch dogs. The dogs jumped a deer on the way and Mr. Hunter shot him.

After hunting a long time, they stirred up the hogs they were searching for, surrounded them, and set their dogs to catch them. But the hogs were ferocious fellows. They cut one of the dogs in the throat so badly that they feared he would bleed to death and wounded several others until the dogs began to be a little afraid of them. Mr. Hunter had dismounted and gone into the hammock on foot when one of the hogs charged him so fiercely that he had to jump up on a stump to get clear. Another one ran Mr. Lyndale out of the hammock, so he told Mr. Hunter to take his rifle and shoot the fattest one and they would try to capture the other. After Mr. Hunter shot one, they had no better success with the one that was left. He led them a long chase and would charge at their horses so furiously that they were obliged to run from him. Their horses made some wonderful jumps but all were getting tired, so Mr. Hunter finished the hunt by shooting the second hog. They had now come up to the Hunters' house to divide the meat.

After they had their suppers, the men set to work cleaning and cutting the animals. Mr. Hunter attended to the deer, while the others placed two logs about a foot apart and built a fire between them. They placed all the kettles and vessels that they could boil water in to clean the hogs on the logs. It was dark long before they finished. George sat on a fence nearby watching them as they moved about the bright fire. It shone on the trunks of the pine trees, making them look like the pillars of some vast edifice, the dome of which was lost in darkness. After the men finished, they divided up the meat.

Since Mr. Hunter and his family had been invited to a wedding, he told George that he must go too. So, at three p.m. the family set out. With George on a pony and Nelly harnessed to the cart in which his two daughters were seated on chairs, Mr. Hunter led the way, riding on a saddle on Nelly's back. They stopped at several of the neighbors' houses and waited until they were ready, so that their company soon increased to quite a train. On the way they saw parties in carts, wagons, and on horseback, all going to the wedding. Several young beaux passed them with their ladies mounted behind them on their horses. At sunset they arrived at their destination, an enclosure with a number of houses surrounding a principal one, and found a great many horses hitched to the fence. Before they even reached the house, they heard a fiddle and tambourine and the stamping of people dancing. When they got into the main house, which was crowded with guests, George was introduced to the host. When George asked him the name of the dance so many people were caught up in, a rude kind of jig, he was told it was called the "Cracker Six" and was such a favorite dance that they danced no other.

Some people had built a large lightwood fire in the yard, and a crowd gathered about it talking. The Hunter males joined the crowd and George listened to the conversation, mostly about crops, rafts and hunts. One enthusiastic old man was telling him on the way to the wedding that his dog had struck a fresh bear track and he had followed it into a swamp but gotten tired out wading in the mud and water without getting a shot at the bear. A party was immediately made up to drive to the swamp the next day. Most of the people had brought their children, and their dogs had followed as a matter of course. The boys were running short races, jumping and wrestling; and the dogs, black, white, brown, tan and yellow—all breeds from the fine hound to the bull—were trotting about, some wagging their tails happily and others with their hair ruffled up and growling. A number of dog fights occurred. Happily, they were the only kind of fight, since the host did not furnish any whiskey.

About eight o'clock, everyone was asked over to another building. On entering it, George found the crowd filling it except a circle in the center. As there was no minister in that vicinity, the family had employed the Justice of the Peace to marry the couple. The Justice stood up opposite the door, with a man on each side of him holding a candle. When the couple to be married came in, the Justice commenced in a loud voice, "Well my friends we are met here to jine . . . ." Here he stumbled a long time over the names and then continued reading in a bad manner the whole of a very long marriage service in which he made some mistakes that set almost every one laughing.

After the marriage, the ladies began going in to supper. It was an hour or so before they had all finished, and then the men started. When Mr. Hunter and George went in, they found plenty of roast pig, chicken, bread, custard, pudding and pie, all made from sweet potatoes and which George relished. After supper, since Mr.

Hunter's party had seen enough, they returned home. The dancers danced until daylight the same unvaried, unending Cracker Six.

The gentleman at whose house the wedding was held owned about fifteen hundred cattle, which was more than he could well attend to. Mr. Hunter offered to take care of about fifty of them. The man agreed. A few days after the wedding, Mr. Hunter stayed at his house all night and in the morning drove them to his own house with the help of two or three others. George was not yet up when he heard the cracking of whips, the shouts of the drivers and the lowing and bellowing of the cattle. He hurried out to see them. There were about fifty, including calves and yearlings. Some of them were very wild and kept the men and horses continually maneuvering to keep them with the rest. Part of the cattle broke away and one of the young men dashed after them at full speed through the woods, when his horse tripped over a gopher hole, fell and threw his rider a long way over his head. But the young man was on his feet and on his horse again in a minute, and they secured all the cattle in a pen which had been built for them.

And now they needed to be milked. The calves were all separated and put into a small pen. After one of Mr. Hunter's daughters came into the main pen with a milk pail, one of the calves was let in. The calf at once ran to its mother to suck. While it was doing so on one side of the cow, the milkmaid, holding her pail in one hand, milked about a cupful from the other side. The cows are so wild when first penned in the spring that this is the only way they can be milked, but they get tamer in a few weeks and submit with less trouble. Some are so wild, though, that they cannot be milked at all. Since the cows live only on what they can pick up in the woods and swamps, they do not provide much milk.

The greatest benefit in penning cattle is derived from the manure. Instead of carting the manure, farmers build their pens by the side of their fields and move them farther along every two or three weeks. With fences easily removed, they can do this easily and have their new land thoroughly manured quickly. Farmers call this "cow penning" the land. The pens are very large and the outside fences are left up to enclose the old pens in the field. The Hunters now had plenty of milk and fresh butter, of which George was very fond.

George had such poor luck hunting wild turkeys that he felt disposed to give it up and own that he was not Indian enough to hunt them. He was satisfied that it needed more care and skill to hunt them than anything else. But Mr. Hunter told him to persevere and he would get one yet. In fact, the same flock that frustrated George was still around the south end of the field and came in to feed every day when no one was working there. George decided to try again, so early in the morning he went to the field and sat on a log under some bushes. He was well hidden but could see up and down the field. After about an hour, he heard turkeys calling in the bushes behind him. He regretted that he could not imitate their call, which all successful hunters found a necessary skill.

He had been listening to the turkeys for a while and wondering where they would come out, when, turning his eyes toward the field, he saw a large flock walking out. He turned, selected the largest gobbler and fired. As he fired, the turkey jumped up several feet into the air and then settled down into a heap. George foolishly rushed out while the birds stood as if paralyzed before flying off into the hammock. He fired at one on the wing but did not bring him down. But since he had secured the finest one of the flock, he got it and started for home pleased with his success.

When he told Mr. Hunter about his experience, the farmer said that, if he had kept his cover, he might have had several shots more before the turkeys had left. The gobbler's tail made an excellent fan, which George preserved carefully for his mother. He also shot a crane, whose pure white feathers also make beautiful fans. White cranes stand from two to three feet high, live on fish, and may be found in all the waters of Florida. Where there are many of them, they may be seen at sunset, all flying to a single tree, on which they roost together until morning. George also shot an osprey, thinking that it was a bald eagle. But the fishy smell of its plumage and its claws satisfied him it was not. The bird was a full five feet from tip to tip of its wings.

CHAPTER X

The bears were now beginning to come out of their winter quarters and their sign was to be found in many places in the woods about the homes. By sign, the hunters mean any trace that game may leave, such as tracks, beds, or marks of feeding. Mr. Hunter showed George where they had pulled the buds out of the palmettos and where they had gnawed bark off trees. Some of these places were astonishingly high up, often as high as a man's head. Several bears had been shot by neighbors, and a great deal of sign seen in a scrub about five miles long and half a mile wide. The farmers organized a hunt and most of the party set out one afternoon for Lake Broward to camp there that night so they could make an early start. Mr. Hunter had agreed to start at daybreak with George and John; the other men described the stands which he and the boys were to fill, because he had never been there.

Everyone was up two hours before daybreak, anxious to get their breakfasts and start as soon as there was enough light. But they were annoyed to find both of the dogs missing. Mr. Hunter thought that they had run off some varmint that had come about in the night and were trailing in the woods. So he blew his horn. When they did not come, he fired his gun three or four times, which soon brought them. Since Mr. Hunter was to take his double barreled gun, George thought he would use the rifle and let John have his own gun. At last it began to get light enough to see the trail, so they set out, George mounted on Nelly and Mr. Hunter and John on foot. The morning was a little foggy with a very heavy dew on the grass.

They had gone northward about two miles along the shore of the lake, when the dogs struck a trail. They seemed so eager that Mr. Hunter said they would wait and see what it was. The dogs followed the trail half a mile, and Mr. Hunter told George and John to remain where they were while he moved to another spot. Soon the dogs ran straight toward Mr. Hunter, though George could see no deer before them. When Mr. Hunter fired, George heard a tremendous squalling and dashed off to see what it was. He found that it was only a fox which Mr. Hunter had wounded and the dogs were finishing.

They now pushed on faster, for they had lost time in killing the fox. As they went on, Mr. Hunter told George that the bear would probably come out at one of their stands, which were the best on the drive. But if it did not, it would keep down in the scrub and swamp. In that case he would plunge into the thickest of it and try to get a shot. But George and John were to keep on the outside of the scrub in the flat-lands, so that if any deer were run out, they would have a chance at them, and also at the bear, who, if hard pressed, might break out. About five miles on, they came to their stands. The stands, on two trails that led from the scrub through a cross hammock to the lake, were near together and of equal importance, as the bears sometime took one trail and sometimes the other. Mr. Hunter took his station at one of them and George and John at the other.

After a half hour, they heard the dogs running something a long way off. Sometimes the noises would die away entirely and then begin again. Dragon and Ruler, who had struck a trail shortly before they reached their stands, had gone off into the scrub. Finally, the sounds all died away for a long time and then they heard a horn. Mr. Hunter answered it at once. After blowing occasionally for half an hour, three of the men who had camped came to him. They said the dogs had tracked a bear, but it had gone off in the opposite direction from the usual one and nothing could be done until the bear dogs came back.

They sat down on a log and talked, listening occasionally for the dogs. At last they heard them in the scrub and, from the increasingly rapid sounds, knew they were in chase. Everyone took stands on the trails, but the roar of the chase passed on in the scrub, so the bear was evidently not coming out near them. Mr. Hunter took Nelly and told George he wanted to head the bear to a point in the scrub and leave Nelly there for him. The men all scattered on the run for other stands. Since George and John did not know where any other stands were, they followed after

Nelly. On the way, Dragon and Ruler ran up to them. George told John to get Nelly while he tried to get the dogs to join the rest of the pack, whose fierce yellings they could now hear distinctly. But Dragon would not go, and Ruler always followed Dragon. George whistled and whooped to them, but they would only run about hunting for trails.

While George was thus engaged, he heard two guns in quick succession and then a loud whoop. The dogs raved more furiously; other guns were fired; and a torrent of noise passed on down the scrub again. Dragon could not stand it. Although he had an aversion to hunting in a crowd, he dashed into the scrub toward the noise. A minute later George heard him open and go yelling along as if he had jumped something. George motioned to John to look out and then ran along the side of the scrub, keeping a little ahead of the dogs. He had run but a short distance when a deer broke out of the scrub between him and John and struck across the flat-lands from the hammock bordering the lake.

The deer was a fair shot for both George and John. George tried to level his rifle, but the palmettos were very high and the deer made high leaps to clear them. While he was trying to sight, John fired. Then George fired. From the deer's movements, he felt sure he had hit him. John then fired his other barrel and the deer kept on his course but was clearly badly hurt. They had him in a fair run, since the flat was half a mile wide. As they followed him, they saw him disappear in the hammock with the dogs close behind. From the noises of the dogs, they realized that he was going straight down to the lake and guessed he would take to it and get clear. John had to dismount at the edge of the hammock, and they stopped to load their guns before entering it. While standing and listening, they heard the men a great distance off in the scrub, calling to each other. Since they could no longer hear the other dogs, they assumed that the bear fight was over.

They followed the noise of the dogs for a short distance and then it ceased. But they kept on tearing their way through the vines and undergrowth and passed through a number of wet places. While they were moving, Ruler came to them.

"See if there is any blood on him," said George.

"Oh, Dragon would not let him touch the deer, and I expect he has driven him off," replied John.

Since Dragon had his bell on, they expected to find him. But they hunted a long time without success. They could not follow the deer's trail either, as the ground was so broken and bushy. George said, "We will get Ruler to show us the way.

Ruler! Ruler! Where's Dragon? Go find him, boy. Go fetch him." And he whistled and snapped his fingers encouragingly.

Ruler understood and went off quickly. They followed for a long distance and then lost sight of him, but soon heard Dragon's bell and his growling. A minute later they heard Ruler yelping and he soon came sneaking back to them. Dragon had evidently punished him for finding him. They soon stirred up the old fellow, lying beside a young buck that he had caught and pulled down. Dragon appeared glad enough to see them, but he would not let Ruler near the deer. He wanted all the glory of it himself.

George had made a very fair shot, but John had only touched him with one buckshot. He said that it was the first time he had ever fired from a horse and that Nelly would not stand still. They made their deer ready to carry. Because he was a young one, they got him out to the edge of the hammock without much trouble and tied him on Nelly. Then they listened a long time, hoping to hear the others. Finally, they were surprised to hear a sound like a gun fired at a great distance to the north, where the hunt had begun. After listening a long time, they heard it again.

"Why," said George, "it can't be possible that they have gone back again and got so far off in the short time that we have been in the hammock."

"It is strange indeed," said John.

"Well, we are nearer home than they are. If we follow the hammock along the lake, it will take us home; or if we let Nelly go her own way, she must know the route and will take us there."

"Oh, I know what those noises were," said John. "They were the falling of trees. There is a logging camp down at the entrance of the lake and it is them we hear."

"That's a fact," said George. "Well let us push on. But stop. I have my horn with me and you know your father said it gave such a keen sound that it could be heard a great way."

George raised the horn to his lips, drew in a full breath, and blew a long high note. It was answered at once by a loud, deep toned horn.

"That's Lyndale's horn. I know it," said John. "It is the heaviest sounding horn I ever heard."

"There, there. Hark!" said George. They heard another horn nearer than the first and , from its peculiar sound, knew it to be Mr. Hunter blowing in answer to them.

They set out at once and, about a mile toward home, came up to Mr. Hunter and several of his neighbors. There were also two horses, with a deer on one. The men were reclining on the grass and Mr. Hunter looked as if he had seen trouble. His shirt was torn and bloody. But he was laughing as they came up and said, "Good for you boys. You have done your duty."

As they sat down on the grass, Mr. Hunter told them that the men had killed a bear. But since it was near the other side of the scrub, one of the men had taken it around to Mr. Pierce's on his horse. In a short time they were joined by some others and then moved on. They drove the hammock along the lake on their way home but jumped nothing. Taking the two deer up to Mr. Hunter's, they divided them as they always did after hunts. The person who shot it has first choice and the hide. The rest is divided as equally as possible among all who went on the hunt. One of Mr. Pierce's best bear dogs had been injured so much that he had to be taken home in a cart with broken ribs.

That night Mr. Hunter told George more of the particulars about killing the bear. He had taken a post in the center of a scrub, so as to run either way. He heard the dogs coming through the scrub and ran a little towards them when he saw the bear. Firing both barrels, he thought both shots hit. But the wounds did not stop the bear. While Mr. Hunter halted to load, the bear and dogs kept on. After loading, he followed in pursuit, thinking at first that he was the only one near the bear but soon hearing four reports of guns from others who had ridden down the side of the scrub and gone into it ahead of the bear. He finally came up to the bear and dogs again.

The medium sized bear was now badly wounded and obliged to turn every few minutes to fight the dogs. Old Caesar ventured too near, and the bear gave him a blow with his paw that broke some of his ribs and tore his flesh badly. After dodging about a while, Mr. Hunter fired two more barrels, which stopped him. Some of the other men coming up finished him, dragged him out of the scrub and tied him on a horse. As Old Caesar was so badly hurt, Mr. Pierce would not hunt anymore and so they all turned homeward.

The time now drew near for George to leave Mr. Hunter's and meet his Uncle James. One evening, he observed, "There are two kinds of hunts I have not been on yet. I have not been on a fire hunt for deer, and I have not seen any alligator hunting."

"The moon is not right now," replied Mr. Hunter. "The deer feed at moon up, moon south and moon down. We want to go some night when the moon rises at nine or ten o'clock at night. Then we can hunt from dark until the moon rises and have the moon to come home with. It is a little dangerous now hunting at night; there are so many calves in the woods that it needs someone who understands it well, or they may make bad work of it."

"Oh, I should not expect to shoot. I only want to go along and see the operation," replied George.

"Did you ever try shooting by night?" asked Mr. Hunter.

"No, sir."

"Well, I want to see what kind of a shot you can make then. I will get my fire pan, shoot first, and then you can try it."

Mr. Hunter got his fire pan, made of large wires clasped and fastened to a rim with a long handle. Selecting some pine knots, he put them into the pan and set them on fire. Then taking his rifle, they stepped out into a dark night. Mr. Hunter took a splinter of wood and, lighting it, told George to stick it in the bark of a pine tree about fifty yards off with the lighted end upwards. George did so and returned. Standing with the handle of the fire pan over his left shoulder, his left arm passing over it, Mr. Hunter held his gun with both hands as usual. He waited until the flame on the splinter went out, leaving a coal, and then, aiming at it carefully, fired and the fiery coal disappeared. When they went over to it, they found that the ball had hit it plumb.

George now tried the same thing and made a very successful shot, although he did not think he would since aiming requires practice in managing the pan with the left arm and using both hands to hold the gun. Mr. Hunter told George about a number of mistakes that he had heard people make on fire hunts. Some were ludicrous and others quite curious. He said that Mr. D., who had been on the bear hunt with them, was headed home one night on his horse and fell asleep. Some men who were fire hunting shone his horse's eyes and fired at it. They missed the horse but shot Mr. D in the leg and had to pay for both his doctor's bill and the time he lost while he was sick. Mr. Hunter said the only mistake he had ever made was in shooting his house cat, which he took for a wild cat.

One morning Mr. Hunter was going to the big field and told George that that if he rowed the large boat up from the orange grove, they would try to shoot some alligators and catch some fish. George and John started that afternoon. On the way they stopped at a pond to catch some minnows and little silver fish, which they put into a pail of water to keep alive for bait. After that, they got the boat at the landing and rowed up the lake to the big field. Since the boat was large, they had no fear of alligators while in it. Mr. Hunter and Mr. Bliss joined them, and they rowed to a cave which they thought would be a good place for fishing. The wind was up and waves washed so hard on the shore that they did not have much success. So they decided to try for some alligators. If the wind went down toward sunset, they could quickly catch all the fish they wanted.

George suggested they go after a large one that had followed him, wanting to punish that fellow for his daring. Since they were not far from the place, they rowed to it and found the alligator there.

"There he comes boolging out of the rushes," said Mr. Hunter. "I will fix him if I can get a crack at his eye."

The alligator came out into the deep water before them and sank.

"We will back up a little and give him a chance to come up," said Mr. Hunter. "There, hold on to the rushes and keep her where she is."

Soon the alligator brought his eyes and the end of his nose slowly out of the water. Mr. Hunter raised his rifle, but after trying to get a good aim, he took it down again and said that the boat moved so much that he could not aim. They pulled in among the rushes where it was steadier. Mr. Hunter tried again and fired. The alligator did not stir.

"I shot a little too high," said Mr. Hunter.

He loaded again, taking great care aiming. As the rifle cracked, the alligator gave a desperate plunge and then dashed about making the water boil around him.

"I took him right in the eye," said Mr. Hunter. "Wait a little, and then we will pull up and get him."

"He looks as if he would get us, if we were out there," said George. "But you know best about it."

In a few minutes they pulled the boat slowly toward him. In his exertions he had reached the edge of the rushes and was still struggling. Mr. Hunter passed a rope under his tail and made it fast, but it was not long enough to bring into the boat and tie. He asked George to hold the end of it, while he and Mr. Bliss rowed, so they could tow the alligator to the boat landing and cut him up to get his oil. George took hold of the rope. As the movement of the boat tightened the line, the alligator felt the tug, opened great jaws adorned with large teeth, and groaned. Startled, George let go of the rope and sprang forward, nearly knocking Mr. Hunter over.

When he settled down again, Mr. Hunter and Mr. Bliss roared with laughing and told him there was no danger. Even though George did not like holding fast to such an ugly looking customer, the men backed the boat up and he took hold again. Several times he almost let go, as the alligator arched his back and groaned horribly. But the young man held on until the landing place, where they all hauled the creature up on shore.

Then they went back so George would have a chance to shoot one. On warm sunny days, the alligators like to crawl out on the bank or on a log and bask in the sun. Finding one lying in the reeds with just his eyes and the end of his nose up, the way they generally lie in the water, the men worked the boat into the rushes where she was tolerably steady so George could take careful aim and fire. The ball struck the water and bounded over the alligator's head. But he did not move. After George loaded again and struck him right, he lashed the water with his tail, tore about among the rushes trying to get into deeper water, and finally lay still. They moved the boat towards him, when Mr. Bliss said. "I don't like the movements of that fellow. Give him another ball and see if you can't wake him up a little." George fired again, hitting him in the side, and he soon became quiet in good earnest. They towed him to the landing like the other, and Mr. Hunter and Mr. Bliss agreed to cut them up and get the oil the next day.

The first one was twelve feet long from the end of his nose to the end of his tail, the other not so large. They were hideous looking creatures, with great jaws full of teeth, strong clawed feet, and tails almost as long as their bodies. They are said to swim close to where dogs or pigs are standing and knock their prey into the water with a blow of their tails so they can drown anything that they can seize. Since the wind never went down, the party gave up its idea of fishing and went home.

The Hunter's house had no front yard and no enclosure about its front. At first, Mr. Hunter was too busy with work of more importance. Once he began thinking about adding to the house, he took no pains to embellish the old one until he had decided what he would do. But his daughters wanted to plant flowers and make some improvement, even to their log house. So they asked the boys to build a worm fence with rails and a rude sort of gate.

George was away when they began it. By the time he returned, they had it nearly finished. When they asked his opinion, he said that it would answer the purpose, but that it was so homely it made no improvement to the looks of the place. He then proposed that they all build a straight fence instead of the worm one. George had noticed the fences at houses in the neighborhood. Though at first he laughed at them for being so far behind the age, he began to realize why they were better suited for Florida than a regular post and rail fence. If a fence had a hole wider than a hand's breadth, piglets could get through it and destroy things. The difficulty in using traditional posts was that sawn lumber was very expensive since no saw mills were near. In order to make the rails tight enough to block the pigs, the holes in the posts had to be drilled so close to each other that most wooden posts split. George had seen a fence that seemed to answer the challenge, and he decided to make this one like it.

He and the Hunter boys cut down a number of straight-grained lightwood trees, dividing them into proper lengths and splitting them with a marl and wedges into the size they wanted for posts. After they brought them to the house with the horse and cart, George laid out the line of the fence, including places for the gate posts and other posts. Using some tough wood, he made pieces about ten inches in length and four in width, then set Jimmy to work boring holes in them with an inch and a half augur, five inches apart. He had John dig holes about two feet deep for the posts, while he sharpened the tops of the posts so that they would fit into the augur holes in the caps.

His posts were not very thick, but the sound lightwood would last a long time. After putting the posts into John's holes and settling the earth solidly around them, the boys added the caps to hold the posts together. Two posts went into each hole, the thickness of a rail apart; then the rails were laid down, with their ends lapping on top of each other. The caps on the tops prevented the posts from leaning apart. In this way they had a straight tight fence, which looked much better than the original zigzag one and used fewer rails.

George had determined to make a handsome piece of work out of the gate. He got a large lightwood post and set it so far down in the earth that it would not shake and could bear the whole strain of the gate. He dug the hole as deep as he could with a spade and then made a wooden scoop to go even deeper. Since the earth was all sand and light-clay, it dug very easily.

He was earnestly engaged in digging on the second day, when one of the boys said two men were coming up the road on horseback. When George turned, he thought one of them looked like his Uncle James. As they came nearer, he was sure of it and rushed off to meet them. Uncle James had returned to Welaka a little sooner than he had expected and decided to come out with one of the boarders to see George. The boys fed their horses and the gentlemen stayed to dinner. Uncle James told George that he wanted him to return to Welaka in a few days because he planned to go up the river to Enterprise. George was sorry to think of leaving, but he promised to come over as soon as Mr. Hunter could conveniently bring him. Since Uncle James and the boarder had to return soon, they could not wait to see Mr. Hunter.

When Mr. Hunter came home that night, he was sorry to hear of George's intended departure: "You will have to go without seeing a fire hunt, as the moon is not right yet. Then, too, I promised that you should have a fawn and I have not seen any yet. I thought I would wait a week or so before I tried to get you one. But perhaps I can get one and sent it over to Welaka when you come down the river. You would not want to take it up there. I had better keep it for you until you leave for home. I will take you over day after tomorrow. I need to go to the big field tomorrow."

"I would like to have one more good deer hunt," said George.

"I would like to go with you but I cannot. I think Mr. Bliss will go with you. Go over early in the morning and see. He will take his dogs too and ride and put them in. Do that and you will have the best chance, as you can go to your stand direct."

"I like Mr. Bliss, but I don't like his dogs. Every time we have had them with us, they have got on trails of wild cats instead of deer. I have no faith in them. But I will try, as I do want another good hunt before I leave."

"I think there are some deer now in the Spring Branch Bay. As that is near Bliss's house, he would probably drive it with you. He knows where the island stand is. It is a sure stand if the deer are jumped anywhere in the east end of the bay and he would probably put you at it, as he would not have time to put the dogs in and get there in case they jumped the deer where they generally do in that bay."

George was off by daybreak for Mr. Bliss's. He found him at his hand mill, grinding hominy, a staple food in the South, for breakfast. Because grist mills are scarce, almost every house has a hand mill. In fact, George had been in the habit of taking daily exercise at the mill since he had been at the Hunters.

Mr. Bliss had work to attend to but said he would not mind having some venison by way of a change. So he agreed to go for a short drive. He saddled his pony, got his gun, whistled to his dogs, and then set out through the dewy grass. There was only one entrance to the island, a palmetto flat with a few pines in the center of the bay, and that was by a very narrow passage that the cattle and hogs had made. Taking George to the passage, Mr. Bliss told him to cross to the opposite side of the oval shaped island, where he would find a trail. If the deer were started anywhere beyond the island, they would come down this trail. He added that he had killed a number of deer there.

George followed the trail a short distance through the bushes and then came out in the island. It contained about three or four acres of palmetto scrub and was one of the most secluded places he had ever seen. An army might be hidden there. He crossed to the opposite side and found the trail. Since he had some spare time, he walked about looking for deer sign. As he looked, he came across a place where a fire had been lighted recently, with bones and other evidence of someone having cooked and eaten there scattered about. George thought it must be the work of Old Tom, a runaway negro who was thus within a half mile of his master's house and probably eating food stolen from his house. He was the last of a company who ran away together. Everyone else had come in of their own accord, except Old Tom, whom his master did not care enough to search for.

George went back to the stand, examined his gun, and sat down on a log. It was a beautiful clear morning. The mocking birds chattered and sang in a variety of notes; and the only other sound was the bellowing of alligators in the Soak, a mile off. Realizing that this was his last hunt, he felt a little melancholy to think he must give up this free sort of life and return to the habits and customs of city life. He started forming some vague ideas of giving up all the prospects and plans which he and his friends had formed for his future and coming to Florida to settle. He still only saw the romance of a life in the woods, for the novelty had not yet worn off and he was an enthusiast though so young.

He was startled from his reverie by the sound of the dogs. They trailed a long time but did not appear to come any nearer. At last he heard them out in the pine woods; they trailed so fiercely that he knew they were after a fox or wild cat again and felt vexed thinking his last hunt should be spoiled by Mr. Bliss's dogs. About to give up and leave the island, he heard the dogs coming toward the island's entrance in full cry. Running toward it, a little way ahead of the dogs, he could see the palmettos shaken by some animal but he could not see it since it kept in the cover.

The dogs ran around some high bushes in the center of the island twice, each time moving closer to George. But he could still see nothing and finally fired where he saw the palmettos shaking. He could not tell if he had hit it, but the animal made off to the thickest part of the bay. From the baying of the dogs, George supposed they had treed it. Mr. Bliss came up about this time and said, "That fool dog Prince always gets after a wild cat when he comes to this bay." He said it was so late then that he would have to go back home. He was sorry, too, for he knew deer were in the bay and they could get them if the dogs would only jump them.

They went back to Mr. Bliss's for breakfast. Dragon had gone with Mr. Hunter to the field, so George would have to go there to get him if he wanted to continue hunting. He had just made up his mind to do so and try a hunt alone, when he saw Mr. Hunter and John coming in the cart. John had been taken sick in the field, and Mr. Hunter was bringing him home. George got into the cart and they all drove home. On the way Mr. Hunter said that, since his day's work was now broken into, he would prefer taking George over to Welaka at once rather than the next day. George told him that it would take an hour to get ready.

They returned to the house and George packed his things. In an hour they were ready, and George bade adieu to all the family and the scenes about him. On the way, George shot a very large snake, called a moccasin, lying on the shore at the side of a pond. At Welaka, he found his Uncle James and all his friends well and pleased to see him. From his looks, they said, the life he had been leading evidently agreed with his health.

David was especially glad to see him and said they must have that hunt now that they had talked of before. The trouble was to finding good dogs. The only possibility seemed a rough fellow, named Hirly, who had some hounds and was often employed by hunting parties, since he knew the country and pretended to be a great hunter. David went to see him and make arrangements. He told George the next day that they would start on the afternoon of the following day, and Hirly would meet them several miles up the river where he had a large boat, which would hold all of the party with the dogs and camping articles.

CHAPTER XI

CAMP ON LITTLE LAKE GEORGE — A DEER JUMPED — A
VEXATIOUS OCCURRENCE — AN ACCIDENT — A SUCCESS-
FUL SHOT — RETURN FROM CAMP — TO ENTERPRISE — EN-
TERPRISE — GREEN SPRING — TO ST. AUGUSTINE — HISTORY
OF ST. AUGUSTINE — THE FORT — COQUINO — ESCAPE OF
WILD CAT — SAILING AND FISHING — RETURN TO WELAKA

The hunting party, which consisted of David, Mr. Hastings, George and Hirly, planned to go to the western shore of Little Lake George. The three young men, having made all necessary preparations, left Welaka in a small boat which contained their camp fixtures and food for two days. They rowed about three miles and, on landing on the lake's eastern shore, found their guide had just arrived on his horse. After they loaded all their things into his large boat, Hirly turned his horse out into a field, got his dogs and luggage on board, and they shoved off. The boat was large and heavy; as the wind was fair, they hoisted the sail which soon carried them across the lake.

They disembarked on a shell hammock, composed of multitudes of small fresh water shells mixed with earth and covered with a heavy growth of cabbage palmetto trees. Since it was almost sunset, they found the frame of a hut there and started making camp. Hirly took his gun and said he would go and try for a turkey. The young men applied themselves to their tent, putting the frame in the proper shape and then stretching over it the blankets and quilts they had brought for that purpose. They left the side towards the fire open, cut palmetto leaves and strewed them thickly over the ground to protect themselves from any dampness, and on these spread their blankets and pillows. Since they had plenty of room in their boat, they had brought pillows with them. Then they gathered enough wood to cook their supper.

By this time it was dark and Hirly returned without any turkeys. They boiled their coffee and sat down at their supper. The guide cut enough wood to keep the fire burning all night, and then they sat around it telling stories and singing songs for an hour or two. Hirly said that while looking for a turkey, he "had seed lots of bar and deer sign and thought they would have good luck on their hunt."

Before lying down, they discovered that the best dog of the three they had brought had wandered off. They were annoyed because they feared he might not be back in time in the morning. The three young men lay down in their tent early, expecting to make an early start. Hirly said the tent was too close for him, so he wrapped himself in his blanket and lay down by the fire. None of them slept very soundly, with the hooting of the owls, other strange noises and the novelty of their position all making them wakeful. Several times during the night the dogs barked and ran off, but they soon came back again and lay down.

Toward morning George slept. When he awoke, he found all the others up. Hirly was making corn bread and boiling coffee for breakfast, although they could hardly see any signs of daybreak. By the time they had eaten, it was getting quite light. As everyone wanted to load their guns afresh, they stepped to the bank of the lake and, one after another, fired their guns in quick succession. The effect of the morning salute was surprising. Their guns sounded like heavy cannon, reverberating from point to point along the lake shore, far down to the river. Just before sunrise and after sunset, echoes are wonderfully loud and clear. Everyone loaded their guns with care and, all things being in readiness, set off for their hunt.

Between the hammock and pine woods was a strip of low ground covered with saw grass. They had to cross this and go about a mile before they came to the place where Hirly proposed to hunt. He would stay there and put the dogs in, while the others moved on to the stands. They walked a mile more along the side of a hammock, and then David put George at a stand. Beyond him a short distance he put Mr. Hastings and took the third stand himself. The dogs soon jumped a deer and ran him through the hammock, past all three of the stands without its coming out at any. It then turned back again towards Hirly; and George heard the guide fire both barrels of his gun, then whoop and blow his horn. Thinking that he had killed the deer, they all left their stands and started towards him. Then they heard the dogs in pursuit of a deer that seemed to be running toward them, so they turned and ran back to their stands.

Mr. Hastings got near enough to his stand to see a deer run out at it, but not to shoot it. As the deer went off, they gave him up and started for Hirly again. On the way they met him.

"Well, did you see that deer?" said he.

"Yes, Mr. Hastings saw a deer. And if you had not called us from our stands, we might have killed it."

"Called you from your stands! Why, I blew my horn and fired my gun to let you know that the deer was coming."

The young men looked at each other. George asked, if that was his signal for a deer coming, what his signal was when he wanted them to come to him.

They were all vexed but had come too far to give up, so they followed the dog which had chased the deer a long way and now seemed to be returning. They all raced for stands, hoping that the deer would strike out of the hammock. But as the dogs came abreast of George and passed on, he saw they were not coming out at his stand. So he ran along, keeping opposite the noise of the chase.

As he ran, he caught a glimpse of the deer, which would cross a little ahead of him. He stooped down so as to be as hidden as possible by the grass and bushes and moved toward a thicket from the end of which he thought to get a shot. Keeping his eyes on the deer to see if it might not take a sudden turn, he never saw a deep narrow ditch that had been worn by the water and was hidden by long grass leaning over it. He fell into it and pitched head foremost against the opposite bank with almost enough force to stun him. When he got up, for a moment he hardly knew what had happened. The cries of the dogs near him, however, revived him quicker than anything else could have; and he picked up his gun and trotted along slowly for his strength had not returned.

All this had taken but a minute, and he was soon at the thicket. But just as he reached it, he heard a gun nearer in to the hammock and then David's voice triumphantly and excitedly cheering on the dogs. As he stepped out beyond the thicket to see what was going on and before he could scarcely breathe, a large buck running at full speed was almost on him. George sprang aside quickly, raised his gun and fired. The deer instantly disappeared in the bushes, and he did not know whether he had hit it.

As the dogs swept past him with their tongues lolling out, George was aware of a singular feeling of faintness coming over him and sank down on the grass. He lost his consciousness briefly. When he recovered, he found the others holding him and sprinkling water on his face. They were all astonished and assumed the buck must have run over him and knocked him down, since he was directly in its tracks. He explained what had happened and asked if they had got the deer. They said no, but the dogs had stopped running and were not far off. Two of them went for the deer, while David stayed with George, who was beginning to feel well again. They found the deer at no great distance. David had mortally wounded him, but George's shot had helped stop him.

After George's injury, they decided not to hunt any more, so they sat down and lunched. They cut up the deer and, except for George, each carried a part. "Now," said Hirly, "if my boat had not been leaky, I would have brought my horse over and that would have saved this trouble." They took a different route homewards, across an uninhabited stretch of land between the St. Johns and Ocklawaha Rivers, running into a great number of deer tracks and bear sign.

On the way home the dogs went off on more trails, but the party kept on for camp, stopping often to rest. Passing through dry grass and leaves, the guide put out fire. Soon a great column of fire and smoke swept down toward the hammock behind them. Hirly said he did it to make the hunting better, since bears and deer like to feed on the fresh young grass that comes up when the land has been burned over in the spring.

When they reached the camp, David and Mr. Hastings took down their tent and stowed things on the boat, while Hirly prepared a glorious feast for dinner. They all rested a bit and then set sail. After switching to the small boat and letting Hirly take the deer home on his horse, they arrived home a little after sunset, well pleased with their trip despite the unpleasant events that had occurred. George still wanted to visit Silver Spring, but Uncle James had determined to go up to Enterprise by the next boat, and from there to St. Augustine. Since he could not plan it then, he told David and Mr. Brown that, if possible, he meant to arrange it at some future time.

On the day they were to go to Enterprise, with the break of day came the Steamer Darlington. While George had already been over the first twenty miles of the route, once they reached the southern end of Lake George, the scenery was new to him. South of the lake, the river became much narrower. Some of the gentlemen got their rifles and went to the bow of the boat to try and shoot alligators sunning themselves on the banks. But shooting from a moving steamboat is not as easy as it seems, and they did not make very successful shots. The ship's captain, who had been shooting them for years, rarely ever missed. When the alligators heard the boat coming toward them, they generally slid into the water before anyone could get within shot of them. As the Darlington moved on, the river became so narrow that the steamship would graze the rushes along the banks whenever it turned.

Enterprise is situated on the north shore of Lake Monroe, a lake about ten miles long from east to west and five miles broad. Directly opposite is Mellonville, formerly Fort Mellon. The river runs into the eastern end of the lake and out at its western end. It was dark when they entered the lake. Landing first at Mellonville, they crossed to Enterprise where they could see the long rows of lights in the hotel windows reflected on the lake. It seemed a strange sight so far up in the wild woods of Florida. They found a large and well-kept hotel, with about forty boarders at the time. People are continually coming and going from Enterprise, often taking a stage for Smyrna and Indian River, Florida's most celebrated hunting and fishing region. When he found that the hotel owned an excellent sailboat, George was out on the lake every day with some new companions. The trolling here, however, was not as good as in the river, because the lake is too shallow in many places.

Although Enterprise consists only of the hotel, a bowling alley, a store, a post office and a few smaller buildings, a great deal of freight is landed here, as well as at Mellonville. Old Enterprise, two miles east of the current town, is an old building formerly used as a hotel but now uninhabited and in a ruinous state. Close by and about a quarter of a mile back is the Green Spring, a great curiosity surrounded by tall palmetto trees among which seats have been made for visitors. Circular, about fifty feet in diameter, the spring is very deep and its water looks as green as the waters of Niagara Falls. Oddly, when taken out, the water seems as clear as water can be.

George would have liked to visit Smyrna and Indian River, having heard stories of the great fishing at those places. But it was now too late in the spring and his uncle had already planned a trip to St. Augustine with a pleasant party. When the day arrived, they found a large party, as it was getting toward the season when most of the boarders leave Enterprise. At Welaka they stopped with Mr. Brown, and David and George found a way to go to Silver Spring. Uncle James had decided to remain in St. Augustine for four weeks, so George could return to Welaka for a week and take the trip.

They reached Pilatka at sunset. Some of the passengers spent the night at hotels; others remained on board. Leaving Pilatka early in the morning, they reached Picolata in a few hours. For years, Picolata, a community of but two or three houses, has been the point at which St. Augustine travelers changed for the Savannah and

Charleston steamers. Having engaged a four-horse stage for the trip to St. Augustine, Uncle James' party found it waiting for them. Since there were six of them, each with a trunk, the stage was heavily loaded. They started together with other stages over a sandy road that in places was covered with water. They had heard that it was a terrible ride, but as the day was delightful, and the road not bad, they enjoyed it. One feature of the ride was new to George. Each driver carried a trumpet or horn from which he occasionally extorted a strain of some negro melody or trumpet call. Some of these drivers play very fairly, which adds to the pleasure of the trip. To an invalid, however, the ride is fatiguing. A new railroad, being built between St. Augustine and Tocoi, a few miles south of Picolata on the river, should help make the trip easier.

George did not expect to like St. Augustine. He had formed a poor opinion of it from reports he had heard and a miserable engraving he had once seen. He was, therefore, surprised and delighted when, on emerging from the sand hills and scrub, he saw a pretty town with white houses and church steeples lying on the opposite side of a narrow river. They entered the town over a long bridge which crosses the river and adjacent meadows. As soon as the driver came within sight of the town, he seized his horn and kept playing until he drew up in front of the hotel. At the sound of the horn, smiling faces of all colors filled the windows. Little negroes danced and hurrahed in the streets; the boarders in the hotels swarmed out on the piazzas; and a general excitement swept through the town. All of this happens despite the fact that during the season there are fresh arrivals daily. Their party found the hotels all crowded, but, by taking poor rooms for a day or so, they were promised better ones soon. Although they were late for dinner, the hotel's proprietor prepared a meal in a short time. After eating, they took a stroll through the town.

Before describing what George saw and did in St. Augustine, we have thought it would be well to give some of the history of the place. St. Augustine, the oldest city in the country, was settled by a party of Spaniards under Pedro Melendez de Aviles in 1565. It is consequently nearly fifty years older than any other city in the United States. One of the principal objects in settling it was to drive out the French Huguenots who had settled on the St. Johns River. Although there was no war between France and Spain, the Spaniards attacked and took the French Fort Caroline, killing all the Protestants who fell into their hands. When several French vessels wrecked on the coast of Florida, south of St. Augustine, the nine hundred survivors, many from the noblest families of France, began walking northward along the coast and were met by Melendez and the Spaniards, who promised protection if they give up all their arms. They did so and were cruelly murdered by the Spaniards near Matanzas Inlet.

The place was captured several times by the English Buccaneers. Sir Frances Drake, sailing up the coast, discovered the look out or tower which the Spaniards had built on Anastatia Island, opposite the city and landed to see what it meant. Finding a Spanish city, he attacked and pillaged it. This look out is still standing, and the United States government has even added another story to use it for a light house. But the building's wall, with its many angles and loop-holes, is Spanish.

The fort, which is the oldest military building in the United States, was begun in 1680.[1] For upwards of sixty years, large numbers of the Apalachee tribe and many convicts worked on it. It is said that the King of Spain had been so often applied to for money to complete it, that he at last enquired if they were building it of gold. Despite all the cost and effort, it was not entirely completed until 1756. Like most of the buildings in St. Augustine, the fort is build entirely of coquina. Coquina, which consists of immense numbers of small shells, mostly broken pieces, cemented together by some unknown process of nature, is quarried on Anastatia Island opposite the city. When first quarried, coquina is generally soft and can be cut into blocks by axes. Over time, exposure to the sun and air hardens it. It is said to be one of the best materials in the world for fortifications, since a cannon ball will sink into it without splitting it.

In 1740 Gen. Oglethorpe of Georgia invaded the place and planted a battery on Anastatia Island, from which he cannonaded the fort but made scarcely any impression on it. The holes where several cannon balls entered the east side are still to be seen, but the balls themselves have been dug out and preserved as curiosities.

The fort forms a square with a bastion at each corner and a tower at the outer angle of each bastion. The tower on the north east corner is upwards of thirty feet high and served as a look out. Surrounding the fort is a ditch, thirty or forty feet wide, which was once twelve feet deep but now is dry. An outwork called the "demi-lune," formed partly by the ditch, protects the entrance on the south side. Visitors enter over a drawbridge to the demi-lune, then by a bridge across the main ditch to the gate, which was formerly defended by a portcullis. Both the drawbridge and bridge across the main ditch have decayed and been replaced by rough timbered ones, but the pillars of the bridges and the beams can still be seen. The square courtyard in the fort's center is surrounded by doors leading into the different apartments and dungeons. Opposite the entrance is the chapel doorway. Its

---

1   Construction of the Castillo de San Marcos actually began in 1672.

entrance was once covered with ornamental carvings, but they have been broken and battered and cannon and mortars now fill the room, where once the Romish priests performed their rites.

In 1763 Florida was ceded to Great Britain, but twenty years later it was restored to Spain. Spain ceded Florida to the United States in 1820, and the Americans took possession of St. Augustine and the fort in 1821. Since it has been in the hands of the Americans, the fort has been allowed to fall into ruin. It seems a great pity that so interesting a military relic as this should fall apart for want of a small expenditure. Even though no repairs have been made to the fort itself, in front of it the government has built a strong water battery, probably of far greater value than the fort in the present state of the science of war. The courtyard has a pavement of coquina, but it lies a foot under soil. An officer who once commanded there had his soldiers bring the dirt in to make a watermelon patch, so local boys could not steal his melons. It is all now overgrown with weeds, which gives the place a deserted look.

Shortly after the fort passed into the possession of the United States, a portion of the north eastern bastion, immediately in the rear of the high tower, caved in and disclosed a walled passage way in the center of the bastion, which had always appeared to be solid earth. This passage connected with two dungeons, in one of which several skeletons and chains were found. The entrance to these dungeons from the neighboring ones had been so skillfully walled up that even the city's oldest inhabitant, it was said, did not know of their existence. In one of those dungeons visitors can see the Treasury Chest, a heavy, iron-bound mahogany chest with three antique locks, about eight feet long, five feet high and five feet wide. St Augustine used the dungeons as a prison for a long time and their walls are scrawled over with names and rude drawings of ships. If the walls of those old dungeons could but speak, what tales of horrid cruelty they would reveal; for doubtless some poor Protestants were walled up alive in them after the manner of the Inquisition.

The room that excites the most attention is the dungeon from which the celebrated Indian chief Coacooche (Wild Cat) escaped. He and his friend Talmus Hadjo were confined in this dungeon in 1837 during the Florida War. Because he had been one of the most active and daring of the chiefs, great pains were taken to secure him. The dungeon is about sixteen feet square; and its only entrance is from the court yard of the fort, where a watch was always kept. A long narrow loop hole opens outward, about eighteen feet from the floor and apparently too narrow to admit of a man passing even his head through. But determined to attempt an escape through it, the two Seminoles feigned sickness and were allowed to go out and get such roots as they wished. These roots reduced their weight, making them very thin. They selected a dark night, made ropes of their bedding; and Wild Cat climbed up to the loop hole. He worked through and, coming out head first, had to descend his rope on the outside into the ditch. His companion did not fare so well; as he descended, the rope broke and he fell and injured his leg so that he could hardly walk. But they found a mule, mounted Hadjo on it and escaped.

St. Augustine is built on a peninsula about half a mile wide and several miles in length. The St. Sebastian River, which cuts it off from the mainland on the southern and western sides, has a bridge for the stages from Picolata. In front of the town, the Mantanzas River separates it from Anastatia Island, which lies between the river and the ocean. The city is about a mile, in a direct line, from the ocean, while the river and island opposite the city are each about half a mile wide. Since the channel for vessels coming from and going to sea passes around the northern end of Anastatia Island, it is a very difficult one to negotiate.

Formerly, the only land entrance to the town was through the city gates on the north side. A ditch and an embankment reached from those city gates to the river on either side. The line of the ditch and the embankment from the gates westwardly are still visible; and the high ornamented pillars of the gates with the sentry boxes and adjoining coquina work are still standing and among the greatest curiosities in the place. The original wooden gates have long ago disappeared.

Since St. Augustine's soil is sandy, the river continually encroaches upon the city and threatens in time to wash a part of it away. To prevent this, the United States government has at a great expense built a substantial wall the whole length of the city. This wall, raised a little above the level of the street on the inside and flat and wide enough for two people to walk abreast, is the favorite promenade for the young people of the town.

Many of the streets are very narrow, with houses built of coquina and then stuccoed and whitened. They are said to be very damp, but as the climate is warm, they are no doubt comfortable. Although many of the people are of Spanish descent, the majority are descendants of the Minorcans who were brought here during the English occupation of Florida.

St. Augustine was once embowered in orange groves. Every house had several trees in its garden, and they bore so profusely that they provided the chief support of many of the inhabitants. But the great frost of 1835 killed all the trees. Others were at once planted, but the orange insect and subsequent frosts have damaged them greatly. Now that we have given our readers some idea of St. Augustine, we will return to George and his uncle.

We left them as they were strolling through the town. After visiting the public square with its monument erected on the occasion of the granting of the Spanish constitution and wandering through the quaint old streets, they went to the river side and paced up and down upon the sea wall until near sunset. They arranged with one of the boatmen to take them and their acquaintances to the beach the next day. Early the following morning everyone collected at the boat landing and, with a fair wind, set sail for the north beach. Landing just inside a point where there were no breakers, they set out to walk along the beach and gather shells.

Who does not love to stroll upon the beach, where the breakers come dashing on in long lines of foam and cast themselves with an expiring effort upon the sandy beach? Wave follows wave with unremitting constancy and regularity. While they look so great and fierce where they first break into foam, they are shorn of their might as they proceed. And when at last they break and scatter on the sands, they glide hurriedly back as if to seek the shelter of the next wave and ride themselves beneath its advancing foam. And how far will one wander without knowing it. You look forward and think there are some beautiful shells just beyond, on that next point; you reach it, find a few and see more still further on; and so you keep going, stopping to see the waves dash upon each point, until you are astonished as you look at your time piece to see how the hours have gone. And so it was with most of the party. But Uncle James could not walk very far, and so George returned with him to the boat.

The boatman said it was a good time of the tide to fish. Since he had bait and lines, they shoved the boat a little from the shore and anchored her. The tide was strong so they used drop lines with heavy sinkers. They had fine sport, for the whiting, an excellent kind of fish and very handsome, bit very fast and they caught a great many. It was a long time before the rest of the party returned. Having wandered so far before they thought of returning, they were very tired but had a large quantity of shells, some of them very pretty but none of them rare.

The following day George and Uncle James went to the long bridge to fish for sheep's head. They caught a number of small fish, none weighing more than a pound. Sheep's head are a hard fish to catch, because they do not snap at the bait but crush and suck it without pulling on it. Since their teeth are large and similar to sheep's teeth, they can break a line unless it is very strong.

The town was filled with visitors, and they had no trouble getting up little groups for sailing parties and other excursions. George was out on the river fishing and sailing almost every day. He had been at St. Augustine several weeks before a party was made up to visit the fort. When people wish to visit, they have to notify the sergeant in charge, who keeps the key, a day or so beforehand. He resides at the United States barracks, large buildings part of which had originally been built for a monastery. Attached to these barracks are a large garden and a cemetery with numerous monuments erected in memory of officers and soldiers, including three pyramids which cover the remains of the officers and soldiers slain in the Florida War.

The sergeant met the party one morning and took them into the fort. He told them the stories connected with the dungeons and showed them the curious things we have described in our history of the town and fort. They looked with surprise at the narrow loop-hole through which Wild Cat escaped and entered with a shudder the dark dungeons in which the skeletons were found. Some of the ladies could hardly be persuaded to enter them, but the sergeant lighted a candle which seemed to struggle in vain against the darkness and gloom of this forbidding place.

A walk on the ramparts of the fort is delightful on a pleasant day, and George was so pleased that a single visit did not satisfy him. He came a number of times with different parties and made several sketches of the fort. When he was at school in the country, George had begun practicing sketching from nature. In St. Augustine, he found such excellent subjects for his pencil that he became quite enthusiastic in it. Besides his sketches of the fort, he made one of the city gates and several of ruined houses.

His three weeks in St. Augustine passed rapidly, as there was always something to be done: a fishing or sailing party, an excursion to the beach, or a ride out into the country. It is true that the rides were not worth much, since the city has only old, broken down stage horses. But George had set his mind on the trip to Silver Spring, and the day to leave St. Augustine found him all prepared. He agreed to meet his uncle at Tocoi and crossed to Picolata in a stage with a number of people going up to Enterprise. After several hours the boat came, and the next day George was in Welaka again.

CHAPTER XII

PREFACE FOR TRIP TO SILVER SPRING — THE START
— A DISASTER — ENTER THE CREEK — THE CAMP —
NO SLEEP — THE CREEK — THE SPRING — ORANGES
— REMAIN A SECOND NIGHT — DISMAL PROSPECTS
— THE WIND CHANGES — FAST SAILING — A FAWN —
GOOD BYE — SAIL FOR HOME — JOYOUS ARRIVAL

George wrote to tell Mr. Hunter that he had returned to Welaka but expected to leave for home with the next steamboat. He thought Mr. Hunter might be willing to catch a fawn for him and bring it over. As he, Mr. Brown and David began preparations for the trip to Silver Spring, Mr. Brown suggested making a new pair of oars. He thought they might have to row a great part of the way, and he did not want to rely on miserable oars, like the ones that belonged to the boat. Although George doubted his ability to make a good oar, he had handled tools a little and was willing to try.

Mr. Brown and he went to the saw mill and found that the best wood available was a thick cypress plank. From this they sawed two strips of the requisite length and width, which they took to David's father's workshop which had all the necessary tools. They roughed out the oars with a hatchet and finished them with drawing knives and shoke shaves. It took a whole day, but they were very pleased with the two handsome and serviceable oars they had made.

Meanwhile, David repaired his boat's sail and caulked up some leaks. George had arrived on Wednesday, and their preparations took another day. Then, since the weather was not right on Friday, they postponed the trip until Monday. Early that morning George was up and carrying all their gear to the platform on the river bank. David soon made his appearance with a list of the articles they had agreed to take and checked everything to see that none were missing.

We will give you his list entire: blankets, axe, guns and ammunition, trolling lines, frying pan, coffee pot, stew pan, plates, cups and saucers, knives, forks, spoons, towels and soaps. Then came the eatables: ham, bread, pork, sweet potatoes, rice, syrup, coffee, sugar, butter, salt and pepper. They did not mean to starve or to want for anything. They stowed their heavy articles in the bows, putting their tightly tied up blankets for the tent and for sleeping on top. Distributing everything else in other parts of the small boat, they found there was no room to spare when they got in. Since there was no wind, they made up their minds for a long row. George took the seat next aft of the mast; Mr. Brown chose the middle seat; and David sat in the stern to steer.

As they were about to shove off, David's younger brothers and their dog Pat watched from the shore. Pat never liked to see any party with guns go off without him, so he sprang into the boat and tumbled about among their legs and the baskets. They started to put him out but realized that he might be useful in guarding their camp and perhaps in starting up turkeys. So they made a comfortable place for him on the top of the blankets and shoved off.

They rowed steadily for two hours, when a little breeze seemed to spring up and let them hoist sail. At first the wind was so light that they could scarcely tell which way it was going to blow, but in a few minutes it became steady and allowed them to open their baskets and lunch off some cold chicken that David had brought. By the time they had completed their lunch, the wind was so fair and strong that the water was dashing from under the bows of the boat. By three o'clock they had reached the western end of Anzie Island, where they landed and George set out to find some lightwood. He soon found an old stump of very fat wood and with Mr. Brown cut it, split it in several pieces and carried it to the boat.

Lightwood does not grow in the hammocks. Almost indispensable for a good camp fire, it is only found in the dry pine lands. The group set sail again and soon entered Lake George. Although the lake was quite rough, a favorable wind allowed them to keep on course, anxious to arrive before dark at the orange hammock at the mouth of the stream flowing from the spring. The wind kept increasing and shifting, so that they were running a little nearer shore than they wished as they approached Yellow Bluff. From their previous trip, they knew how shallow the water was there but still thought it deep enough for their small boat. They were dashing along rapidly, when the boat struck a sand bar and the next wave washed them on it. Everyone sprang into action, David letting the sail run out and George and Mr. Brown seizing oars to push with. But the large waves smashed wildly on the bar, and Pat bounced around the boat, interfering with their movements. They finally shoved the boat off, but not before two waves broke over the sides, soaking them and their bedding and leaving the boat ankle deep in water. There was no serious damage, but they were uncomfortable and their prospects for a dry bed uncertain.

They got the boat under way again and bailed out the water. Poor Pat lay in the bottom of the boat, evidently very uncomfortable, and eyed the water under the slats beneath him as it washed about with each roll of the boat. The sun set and left them still coursing along the shore, anxiously scanning each indentation. Some people had reported not being able to find the entrance, which made them a little nervous. They had been told that the creek might be recognized, because it emptied into a little cave and had tall rushes growing in it and an orange grove to its south. At last David sang out, "There are tall rushes."

"Yes," said George, "and there are oranges to the south of them." They headed for the shore and now dashed along at a great rate before the wind. As they ran through the rushes, taking little channels, they noticed that the water had a different color from the lake. Near shore, they saw it became transparent, and they were satisfied they had found the right place.

They ran their small boat on to the southern point, a solid bed of pure white snail shells. Mr. Brown sprang ashore but soon came back and said they had better run the boat around into a cove inside the mouth of the creek. They did so and found a better and more secure landing place. All now bustled about in different directions to find a good place for their camp. Mr. Brown went but a little way, when he called to the others, who found him standing next to the frame of a camp built by some former visitors. It was in a good place in the grove and would save them the labor of making one. Since it was getting dark, they were obliged to make their preparations in haste.

While David unloaded the boat, Mr. Brown and George looked for some wood but found nothing except a few large orange trees which some reckless person had cut down. The trees were dry, so they carried them to the camp, hoping that, together with the lightwood, there would be enough to last them through the night. George and David soon had the tent rigged up. The frame they used was a palmetto shelter such as the Indians make. Four foot long leaves from the low palmettos are cut and laid over each other like shingles, the points all being downward. When done properly, they are proof against any ordinary rain. George stripped off the old leaves, which were very dry, and made a bed of them after breaking off the large stems.

They found an acceptable bench, then they rigged up a rough table with a board that George had thrown into the bottom of the boat for that purpose. Having now completed all the urgent work, they began boiling some rice and making coffee for supper. Rice was one of the best things they knew of to bring on an excursion like this because it is easily carried and cooked and tastes so good to a hungry man. After supper, Mr. Brown and David took their guns and some lightwood torches and went on a voyage of discovery through the orange grove. George remained at the camp to keep up the fire, dry their bedding, and answer as a beacon if they got lost. After half an hour, they returned and said they could find no end to the grove. They found a number of trees that were evidently bitter sweets, because the country people who come every year to pick them had marked them but had left few oranges on them.

They talked about the next day, hoping the wind would moderate enough in the afternoon to allow them to go home. They did not want to remain over Tuesday night, for George feared he would not get back to Welaka in time for the steamboat and Mr. Brown had important letters he wished to write for the boat's mail. They lay down early and slept until the mosquitoes, which can be found in a Florida hammock at any season of the year, attracted by the fire, gathered thickly to the unusual feast spread out before them. Then George began to regret that he had not brought a mosquito net. They tossed and turned, grumbled and slapped their faces. But it was no use. And so about one in the morning, they all turned out, sat down before the fire and talked over their troubles.

George suggested having some hot coffee, which was agreed to by all. As George had proposed it, he went to work to make it. But it was his first attempt and he placed the coffee pot too close to the flames. In a few minutes he heard a great sputtering, ran to it and found that the nozzle of the coffee pot had melted off.

"Now you have done it," said Mr. Brown. "No more hot coffee this trip."

"That is too bad," replied George. "But can't we repair the damages?"

Mr. Brown looked at it and said, "Put a dough plaster over it and bake it a little. That may answer."

David suggested driving plugs into the holes which would make it stronger. So they cut plugs and drove them into a large dough plaster and dried it all a little. Filling the coffee pot, they soon saw it would answer every purpose, except that they were obliged to pour the coffee out at the top. They laughed over their work as they drank down their coffee. But the conversation got dull, so they all lay down again, hoping to sleep notwithstanding their tormentors.

At daybreak they were all up. David and Mr. Brown took their guns to find out what Pat had been barking at so furiously during the night. George cooked breakfast while they were gone. A little while after the others left, he heard Pat barking loudly and two gunshots, one soon after the other. Although he hoped they had hit turkeys, when they returned they threw down two possums, and he laughed heartily. They ate breakfast hurriedly and soon started in their boat for the spring they had come so far to see.

The stream or creek was a hundred yards wide but almost completely choked up with bonnets and other aquatic plants. They forced the boat slowly through this mass of plants and leaves, hoping to find a channel. After a short distance, the creek narrowed and had a clear channel in the center. Orange and cabbage palmetto trees hung over the shore, and wild duck and other water fowl filled the little pools surrounded by lily pads. The water, from three to fifteen feet deep and as clear as crystal, had great numbers of trout, mullet, catfish, bream, and gar fish. If they had thought to bring a spear or gig, they could have caught as many as they wished.

They paddled up the stream, shooting ducks and whacking the large, saucy fish with their oars, occasionally stopping to admire the strange wild scenery. About a mile from the lake they came to a cove and saw water boiling up two or three inches above the surface. Mr. Brown and George were standing up, paddling carelessly along towards the boil. When the boat reached the center of the spring's core boil, they caught a glimpse far, far down into the quivering waters. Both sank to the bottom of the boat with the same kind of shrinking feeling that would make anyone recoil who suddenly and unexpectedly came upon the edge of a great precipice. Grasping the sides of the boat tightly, they looked at each other in mute surprise as the force of the water whirled them to the far side of the core. Once they found words for their astonishment and delight, they rowed across the spring again. Far down through the pure waters, the bright blue bottom looked like a sky beneath them. They caught glimpses of large fish darting about and saw huge aquatic plants growing from the spring's side and waving their long leaves in the boiling water. Since the force of the boil carried the boat to the sides of the cove, they could remain over it for only a minute.

The entire cove was about fifty feet in diameter, and the boil covered about half of it. Filling a bottle with shot, they tied it to a trolling line and tried to find the bottom of the spring. But before the line could run out, they found themselves pushed to the side of the spring and their line caught among the plants. The water, a little warmer than the lake, was not unpleasant to drink and had no mineral taste. They rowed back and forth over the spring, until they thought it time to go if they expected to get home that day. Reluctantly, they left this strange and beautiful sight and turned their boat down stream.

They reached their camp in a short time, having found a clear channel all the way down. It was so close to the bank and overhung by trees that they had overlooked it earlier. They walked down to the lake shore to see if the wind had moderated, but the waves rolling in were huge and the wind as strong as ever. They hoped it might weaken at dusk so they could go home by starlight. While they waited, they went into the grove and filled a large bag with bitter sweets and cut some canes. Then they fished a while and caught some nice bream. Since there seemed no chance of going home that night, they cut wood and prepared to pass another night in their camp. Cooking their bream and boiling some rice, they enjoyed supper while the wind kept roaring among the trees and the waves washed up on the shore like a small ocean.

George worried that his uncle would be troubled about him if he were not on the steamboat, and Mr. Brown feared he would not be able to send his letters. Finally fatigued, they slept a little more this night than the previous one. As soon as it was light, Mr. Brown went to the shore and reported back that the wind was worse than ever. Fortunately, they had plenty of rice, so there was no danger of starving. After breakfast, George walked down to the shore and thought the wind and waves were subsiding and that the wind was shifting more southward. He returned in haste, told Mr. Brown; and they all went to look again.

"The wind is changing," said Mr. Brown. "Pack up quickly, boys, and let's be off, for every moment is worth something to us."

Packing everything up and stowing it on board by seven o'clock, they were able to shove off from the shore and hoist sail. With the wind right aft, as favorable as it could have been, the boat dashed before it, over waves which were still pretty large. They passed Yellow Bluff and Orange Point and then headed across for Rocky Point, the only dangerous stretch because they had to cross a part of the lake which was several miles from shore. The wind and waves began rising again. Near the center of that long stretch, the wind blew the sail down. That accident actually proved fortunate for them, because they had scarcely taken it all in when a great gust struck them that would have carried the sail out of the boat had it been spread.

Since it seemed foolish to drift before such a fair wind, they hoisted the lower part of the sail but not the spit which raises the peak of the sail. This way they could sail as fast as they wished without any danger. They passed Rocky Point and were soon out of the lake and into the river, where the waves were much smaller. Here they hoisted the full sail again and reached Welaka at noon. They had sailed twenty five miles in five hours.

George had time to get his dinner and call upon several of his closest friends to say goodbye. At the wharf he found Mr. Hunter and John and, to his great delight, a box in which was a beautiful spotted fawn. Mr. Hunter said they had caught it after a hard chase. They had had it only three or four days, but it was quite tame and would eat from their hands. George gave them some of his hunting gear as keepsakes and talked about returning to Florida again, promising, if he ever did, to come and see Mr. Hunter and family.

The steamboat arrived on time. After bidding all his friends goodbye, George went on board and the boat was under way again in a few minutes. Although he felt almost sad as he took his last look at a place where he had spent so many happy hours, when the boat rounded the point he realized that he was now on his way home. He had been so busy for the past several weeks that he had hardly had time to think of it.

The next morning the boat stopped at Tocoi, where Uncle James came aboard. Landing during the night at Jacksonville, they called on their friends and bade them goodbye. The next day they were on their way to Charleston by a steamer that took the outside passage. From Charleston, where they remained only one day, they took a side wheel steamship for New York. Aside from one storm, the weather was bright and clear. George's fawn attracted a great deal of attention, and the passengers loved feeding it.

They left Charleston on Wednesday afternoon at four; by Saturday morning at daybreak they were opposite the Quarantine on Staten Island. Within an hour they were in a carriage at the dock. Leaving their trunks and the fawn to be brought by a cart, they reached home just as Mrs. Morton and Willie were coming downstairs to breakfast. As the door opened, George caught sight of his mother and cried out, "Here, mother, here we are all safe and sound!"

A happy party gathered around the breakfast table that morning, and George had so much to talk about that he could not find time to eat. When the fawn arrived, they had the box taken into the yard and opened it at once to let the poor little creature out. It seemed delighted at having room to run about once more. Later, George had it taken into the country where it became a great pet with all who saw it. Mrs. Morton said that George had grown so much heartier and looked so healthy that she was satisfied with his trip. For many months afterwards, George told his family and friends stories about all his adventures during his trip to Florida for health and sport.

AFTERWORD

MANUSCRIPT PROVENANCE AND DESCRIPTION

Although we know a good deal about Frederic W. Dau, the editor and book and manuscript collector who gave this manuscript to Rollins College in 1955, there is far less information about the author, Cyrus Parkhurst Condit. Born in 1880, Frederick Dau received his education from the U.S. Naval Academy. After completing his service, he edited the *Mortgage Reporter* and the *New York Social Blue Book* and contributed to newspapers and magazines on mortgages, appraisals and real estate. As the owner of one of the largest private libraries in America, he specialized in rare New York and Florida items. A historian himself, Dau published *Florida: Old and New* in 1934. During the 1930s, he befriended A. J. Hanna (1893-1978), a well-known Florida scholar and Professor of History at Rollins. In 1955 Dau donated Condit's original manuscript to the Mills Memorial Library at Rollins College along with several other rare items.

Written on one side of 162 folio leaves (12 5/8 by 8 inches), the manuscript is folded in quires and sewn and bound in stiff tan wrappers. The sewing has come loose, as have the wrappers, but everything is present, including a portion of the spine. The manuscript is enclosed in a brown cloth slipcase. The wrappers and first and last few pages are damp-stained, obscuring only two or three words of the "Table of Contents."

A note on the verso of the front cover identifies Cyrus Parkhurst Condit as the author. It appears to be his first and only literary work. Born on February 5, 1830, Cyrus Parkhurst Condit, the third child (of eight) of Wickliffe Sayre Condit (1795-1872) and Esther Parkhurst (1801-1890), lived in Newark, New Jersey. On May 23, 1855, he married Sarah J. Champlin, who was born on April 14, 1834 in New York City and died on August 26, 1889 in East Orange, N.J. Together they had two children: Agnes Louise Condit, who was born on May 28, 1856 in Newark, N.J. and died in Newton, N.J.; and Sarah Adeline Condit, who was born on September 8, 1858 in Newark, N.J. and died in South Orange, N.J. Cyrus Condit passed away at age 30 on January 6, 1861.

Cyrus Condit's ancestor John Condit immigrated from Wales in 1678 and settled in Newark, where he died in 1713. Two other John Condits are also listed in the family tree. The second, born in 1701, was the grandson of the senior John Condit and Cyrus' great-great-grandfather; he lived through the American Revolution and reached 82 years of age before dying in 1783. His grandson, the third John Condit (1766-1803), was Cyrus's grandfather. He died at 36 in Savannah. Since the manuscript came from New Jersey and since his daughters died in New Jersey, Cyrus P. Condit also appears to be related to Dr. John Condit (1755-1834), a New Jersey physician and congressman listed in the *Dictionary of American Biography*. It may well be through the connection originating from his grandfather that Cyrus Condit was able to visit Florida via Savannah.

We have used an 1855 date for the novel on the basis of internal evidence, Condit's biography, and historical events. (The only date in the manuscript is 185- on a letter in Chapter II.) Since the large hotel the author describes in Enterprise must have been the Brock House, built in 1854, and since Condit was married in the spring of 1855, he must have made the trip on which the story is based in the winter of 1854-55. If the work had been written after December 1855, when the Third Seminole War began, the author would certainly have treated the threat of a Seminole attack more seriously and the settlers in and around Welaka would have been far more cautious.

LITERARY CONTEXT

The year 1855 was a memorable one for American literature. The highly respected poet and newly retired Harvard professor Henry Wadsworth Longfellow published *The Song of Hiawatha*; the struggling novelist Herman Melville serialized *Benito Cereno* in *Putnam's Monthly*; and the itinerant journalist Walt Whitman gathered twelve of his poems together for the first edition of *Leaves of Grass*. Of course, not all that year's work is quite so memorable. On June 25, The New York *Times* surveyed a group of more typical new works that ranged from domestic novels like John Beauchamp Jones' *The Winkles* and Sarah Stickney Ellis' *My Brother; or, The Man of Many Friends* to potboilers like Emma Dorothy Eliza Nevitte Southworth's *The Missing Bride; or, Miriam the Avenger* and historical romances like William Bernard MacCabe's *Florine, the Princess of Bergundy*.

As Longfellow's nostalgic poem, Melville's troubling and ambiguous racial novella, and Whitman's sensual celebration of individualism suggest, the mid-nineteenth-century Northeast literary establishment was struggling between the country's past and its future as it attempted to define the national character. The Alamo and Gold Rush had already begun shifting the nation's expansionist imagination westward—in 1855 the first railroad train would cross the Mississippi—and soon after the Civil War the American West would emerge as the psychic universe in which writers could construct and explore American myths. The West came to symbolize the unlimited potential of the United States and to provide an elemental landscape in which men could achieve and test their manhood, define the fundamental tenets of good and evil, and demonstrate the epic story of the inevitable expansion of Western civilization and its values, or at least the American version of those values.

But for the first half of the Nineteenth Century, Florida served much the same purpose for a different set of myths and legends, those focusing on exploration, contact, settlement, and transformation. The southernmost frontier of North America offered a young nation attempting to secure its place among the European powers a darkly mysterious, exotic history of its own, with almost 300 years of adventure, intrigue, and romance. Florida's earliest novelists found a rich source of material in La Florida's eclectic human stew and bloody adventurous past. From lurid tales of piracy and heroic accounts of exploration to the epic struggle of European colonizers and vast Indian wars, North America's southernmost edge presented to

America's first post-colonial novelists a culturally heterogeneous frontier with a flexible identity which they could shape into their vision of their country's story.

Although Florida has the longest literary tradition in North America, a remarkable collection of poetry and prose dating back to the early Sixteenth Century, its first novel did not appear until 1801. Oddly enough, that book appeared in Paris as the product of a French aristocrat, a Knight of Malta. François-René, vicomte de Chateaubriand, a twenty-third generation descendent of a Breton baron who fought with William the Conqueror in the Battle of Hastings in 1066, was, however, also a younger son, actually the tenth of ten children, who received his own title later in life from the Bourbons. Originally intended for the priesthood, one traditional fate for younger sons of the nobility, he seems to have had a crisis of faith and joined the army instead, the second option.

Chateaubriand hunted with Louis XVI but sympathized with the French Revolution until, disgusted with its excesses, he visited the United States. There he dined with George Washington and took a 3,500 mile trek along the edge of the wilderness to meet Native Americans. Expecting to find the ideal primitive people Rousseau had portrayed, his first encounter was with a group of Oneidas learning European dances from a Frenchman.

After returning to Europe and being wounded as part of the fight against Napoleon, Chateaubriand spent seven years in England teaching, writing and reading British literature. He finally returned to Paris in 1800 to reconcile with Napoleon and establish himself as a professional writer. On April 3, 1801, *Atala, ou les amours de deux sauvages dans le desert* appeared and earned him immediate fame, racing through five editions and multiple translations its very first year in print. *Atala*, the elegiac story of the young Natchez warrior Chactas, the Seminole maid Atala, and saintly French missionary Fr. Aubry, reinforced the myth of Florida as a natural paradise which humans are doomed to lose.

Perhaps because Chateaubriand apparently never actually reached Florida in his long trip through North America, the vicomte's descriptions of its flora and fauna, like those of many other writers who never saw the region, are heavily influenced by William Bartram's *Travels* (1791), which he had translated while in England. After a distinguished and highly successful life as a writer, diplomat and epicurean—his personal chef named a thick cut of tenderloin after him—Chateaubriand died during the Revolution of 1848 as a national hero.

While exploring the effects of Europe's contacts with and settlements in the New World, Florida's first novelist helped define the characters, tone, and themes that would shape much of the state's early fiction. Combining his own experiences on the American frontier with a literary sensibility formed by classical and contemporary writers, he wrote a novel that became an international sensation and inspired generations of Romantic novelists. *Atala*'s accounts of the American Indian's noble savagery and its elegiac tone would permeate much of our frontier literature and set a model for exploring the psychological, social, and emotional consequences of the Euro-American invasion and hegemony of the New World's Garden of Eden.

Three decades after *Atala*, the Rev. Michael Smith's *The Lost Virgin of the South* appeared in 1831 under the pen name Don Pedro Casender. Published in Tallahassee by a Florida resident and set largely in the state, *The Lost Virgin* is an extraordinarily confusing work in which a largely incoherent plot and incredible characters—the title character, captured as a child by Seminoles, finds a Bible which she uses not only to teach herself to read but to convert herself to Christianity—exist mostly to exalt Andrew Jackson.

Smith does show enormous sympathy for Native Americans, including one 28 page theological debate between a Presbyterian minister and a Creek warrior, which the remarkably well read Indian wins by quoting both Alexander Pope and the Emperor Constantine. Robert Montgomery Bird, on the other hand, has little positive to say about Native Americans or anyone else in his scathingly picaresque *The Adventures of Robin Day* (1839). Bird, who would eventually became a Professor of Medicine at the Pennsylvania Medical College and an early experimenter in photography, targeted James Fenimore Cooper's Leatherstocking saga and its complex but heroic portrait of America's natives in most of his work, especially *Nick of the Woods* (1837). The preface to his 1852 reprint of that novel, for example, dismissed Indian culture in Hobbesian terms as "ignorant, violent, debased, brutal."

In Robin Day's picaresque adventures, almost every character is ignorant, violent, brutal, or naïve. Whether planning schoolboy pranks, fleeing the law or volunteering to defend the young American Republic in the War of 1812, little goes right for the boy who washed onto the shore of New Jersey in a shipwreck. When he tries to enlist in a military unit to defend the United States during the war, for example, he finds that he has accidentally joined a British loyalist militia marching against the American army. His misadventures in that campaign include capture by both Indians and pirates before he finally discovers his noble Spanish heritage.

Like Chateaubriand, Smith and Bird, most of these first novelists were fascinated by Indians, pirates, and the rich racial diversity of early Florida, often mixing them together in their work. South Carolina's prolific William Gilmore Simms, whom Edgar Alan Poe considered America's finest novelist, focuses on conflicts and conciliation between cultures centuries earlier in *Vasconselos: Romance of the New World* (1853). At the end of the novel, set in sixteenth-century Cuba and Florida, he offers a romantic vision of hope and harmony when his Portuguese hero Philip Vasconselos marries the Indian Queen Cocalla.

Simms' other Florida book is only partly fiction and has a far less happy ending. A historian as well as a novelist, Simms combines both his interests in retelling the tragic story of the French Huguenots' attempts to establish a colony in the New World in *The Lily and the Totem* (1850). Although not actually fiction—he actually calls it a "series of sketches" on the title page—Simms embellishes liberally, especially when he believes it necessary "to supply the deficiencies of the record" ("Epistle Dedicatory, iv). South Carolina also provided James Burchett Ransom with the inspiration to take the same broad approach to his biography, *Osceola* (1838), aimed largely at a young audience. It was in Charleston that Ransom first saw Osceola at a theater, where the officers in charge of the captured Seminole brought him to see a play. Ransom's life of the great guerilla leader includes tales he claims to have heard from people involved in the Florida War.

Pirates proved an equally attractive subject, especially to the popular novelists of the time. Joseph Holt Ingraham, a well established writer of historical romances, published *Rafael, or; The Twice Condemned: A Tale of Key West* in 1845. Set largely in the waters between Cuba and Key West, the vengeful buccaneer Rafael escapes death only to be recaptured by Cuba's even more vengeful governor. The book's protagonist resembles not only the rebels and pirates who had filled Ingraham's earlier novels, but the Biblical heroes who would dominate his work after he became an Episcopal priest in 1852.

In 1847, Edward Zane Carroll Judson, writing under his pen name Ned Buntline, published *The Red Revenger; or, The Pirate King of Florida*. While Ingraham had set his adventure only a few years before, Buntline had his pirate king ravage the coast 300 years earlier. Buntline, who had served in the U.S. Navy's Mosquito Fleet during the Second Seminole War, combined writing with politics through much of his life. He was not only one of the first dime novelists, writing over 400 during his lifetime, he also helped found the Know Nothing Party and inspired the nativist gangs of New York to start the Astor Place riots.

After serving as a sergeant in the Civil War—he later promoted himself to colonel—Buntline moved to the West and introduced his readers to a young scout named William F. Cody, but whom he renamed Buffalo Bill. Like most of his work, *The Red Revenger* reads like a boy's adventure story, filled with fabulous palaces built into cliffs, alluring women and exotic figures with names like Rinard, Gaspar and Chico the Dwarf.

Pirates also inspired authors of shorter fiction, like John Howison's story "The Florida Pirate" (1823) and William Henry Herbert's novella *Ringwood the Rover* (1843), set in 1659. In almost all the stories, the title character has suffered some traumatic event that drove him to piracy. As he challenges authority—in Herbert's case, Reginald Ringwood threatens to kill Juan de Melendez' daughter if the governor does not surrender St. Augustine—the protagonist offers opportunities for the author to thrill audiences with language that blends archaic forms, bloodthirsty threats and breathless syntax. Ringwood, for example, makes this vow if the city is not surrendered: "And for the girl—thou shalt behold her undergo things, fifty—nay! but fifty thousand times more terrible than death protracted and made horrible by the most lingering torments!" (12)

America's most famous novelist, James Fenimore Cooper, reinterpreted that tradition of piracy with *Jack Tier; or, The Florida Reef* (1848). Originally published as Cooper's only serialized novel two years earlier, the story tells of Captain Stephen Spike's attempt to trade smuggled gunpowder for gold during the Mexican-American War. As the aging but still wily Spike attempts to elude American naval frigates and survive hurricanes, this modern pirate plots to sell his ship to Mexican adventurers, pressure a young passenger into marrying him, and then retire to Mexico with his gold and new wife.

While many critics find *Jack Tier* simply a retelling of similar stories in *The Red Rover* and *The Water Witch*, Cooper's use of a contemporary Florida setting, both among the Tortugas and, especially, Key West in the work's last section, contrasts sharply with most of the other early novelists. The writer's fascination with Key West, "a town yet in its chrysalis state" (481), suggests the appeal of what was soon to be the wealthiest per capita city in the United States, due largely to its wreckers salvaging goods from ships smashing off the Florida Reef. As might be expected from the writer who became our first important national novelist, Cooper also uses his story as a way to explore everything from race and religion to sexual identity and America's destiny.

The same year that *Jack Tier* appeared in book form, Ned Buntline became the first person to publish a second novel about the state, *Matanzas; or, A Brother's Revenge: A Tale of Florida*. Although it claims to be a fictional version of the same stories about the Huguenots that Simms would retell far more accurately two years later in *The Lily and the Totem*, Buntline's history is mostly imaginative. He sets the story in 1548 on Isla Anastasia, assuming that the Spanish have already settled Saint Augustine and built a second fort on Anastasia.

In the dime novelist's adventure, a corrupt priest uses threats of the Inquisition to control the Spanish governor and garrison at the fort on Anastasia. When a group of French Huguenots wreck off the coast and are rescued by the governor's daughter Elisa, Padre Sabano recognizes an uncle, Baron Ludovico de Gourges, and cousin, Edouart, who had refused to help him years before. Imprisoning the governor, baron and his son, Fr. Sabano plots the seduction of Elisa and crucifies the French crew as heretics. The baron's second son, Dominic, comes to the rescue, crucifies some of the Spanish troops in retaliation, and has the "demoniac priest" branded with a cross on his brow and coiled serpents on his cheeks.

The de Gourges family sail off to establish a peaceful colony on the Mississippi near Natchez, along with the governor, a new Protestant convert, and his daughter, Edouart's new wife. Ten years later the renegade priest, now a great Indian Medicine Man, leads his new tribe to attack and slaughter the peaceful Huguenots, including the parents, Eduoart, and Elisa's two children. This time, Dominic gains his final revenge but Elisa soon dies of a broken heart.

Buntline, who never had problems with altering historical facts, has made significant revisions in the story of the Huguenot expeditions of 1562 and 1564. During the second journey, the colonists' leader, René de Laudonnière, established Fort Caroline near present day Jacksonville. Concerned about the French presence in what they saw as their territory, the Spanish sent Don Pedro Menéndez de Avilés the following year to establish a new settlement at Saint Augustine and remove the interlopers. After surrounding most of the Huguenots at Matanzas Inlet, Menendez promised them mercy but slaughtered almost all of those who surrendered in what has become known as the Matanzas Massacre. Looking for revenge, Dominique de Gourgues, a captain in the French army, organized a successful attack in 1568 on Fort Caroline, now in Spanish hands, burnt it and killed all his Spanish prisoners.

Aside from Michael Smith and Ned Buntline, the only other early Florida novelists known to have lived in the state was a leading voice for the antebellum Southern way of life. Like her great rival, Harriet Beecher Stowe, Caroline Lee Whiting Hentz was born in Massachusetts and moved to Cincinnati in 1832, where the two women became close friends. Eventually Hentz moved to North Carolina and, finally, Marianna, Florida, where she wrote her two last novels, *Marcus Warland* (1852) and *The Planter's Northern Wife* (1854).

Although the latter, her explicit answer to Stowe's *Uncle Tom's Cabin*, became her best known work and the most popular of the anti-Stowe, anti-Tom fictions, *Marcus Warland* covers much the same material in the more explicitly Floridian setting of Long Moss Spring. This story of a young man who rises from poverty to success in the law offers her many opportunities to attack abolitionist views and offer an apologia for both slavery and the plantation system.

Another admirer of the plantation culture, Georgia's Francis Robert Goulding, who would later edit *The Soldier's Hymn Book* (1863) for confederate troops, wrote the work closest in subject if not in spirit to *A Trip to Florida for Health and Sport*. Second in popularity only to Chateaubriand's *Atala*, Goulding's *Robert and Harold; or, The Young Marooners on the Florida Coast* (1853) went through nineteen editions in slightly over half a century. The title is slightly misleading, however, since the book actually tells the story of four young people, ranging in age from seven to fourteen, accidentally stranded on what seems to be a barrier island south of Tampa in 1830.

Strongly influenced by *Robinson Crusoe*, *The Swiss Family Robinson* and Shakespeare's *The Tempest*, Goulding's novel shows how four devout youths can not only survive but impose their will on the wilds of Florida by combining faith, resilience, diligence, and ingenuity with practical knowledge based on experience, observation and reading. Accidentally marooned in a remarkably well equipped boat—it carries everything from goats and books to medications and an umbrella—three Georgia siblings and their cousin spend months learning woodcraft and demonstrating Christian virtues, while they search for a way back to their family wintering in Tampa. Their success is demonstrated at the end when they rescue their parents whose ship has been wrecked in a hurricane while searching for the missing children.

Aside from focusing almost entirely on the dynamics among the four children—they interact with only a single Floridian and a couple of soldiers from Tampa's Fort Brooke—*The Young Marooners* differs primarily from Condit's novel by emphasizing the ways its young people call upon what they already know from books or earlier lessons to tame their wilderness. Where George Morton constantly learns new skills and gains new knowledge from his experiences in Florida and his mentors, especially Mr. Hunter, all four of the young marooners call upon their collective knowledge in a book that its author, a Presbyterian minister, clearly wishes to reflect his belief that God's providence will always bless those with "brave hearts and steady hands." (416)

CHARACTERIZATION

The hero of *A Trip to Florida for Health and Sport*, George Morton, finds his sheltered life in a country boarding school disrupted by his father's death a year before the story begins. After his protective mother decides to move him home to New York City, he develops a cold and cough, clearly external, physical symptoms of his psychological and emotional sense of loss, displacement and uncertainty. When his Uncle James offers to take him to Florida for his health, even his mother reluctantly agrees.

It seems hardly accidental that George spends part of the voyage south ill and inside protective walls, either in his own cabin or the First Engineer's cabin on deck, separated from nature, or that one of his first experiences is to see a ship beached and its displaced passengers rescued. Only when this first stage of the journey, with its repeated parallels to the protagonist's condition, ends in Welaka can the author begin George's Florida odyssey of regeneration and growth.

At first, George's physical and mental health place limits on his activity and development. On one of his early deer hunts, for example, he hesitates to go out in the rain until he is offered a horse. At another time his companions, worried about his health, stop him from going on an evening fire hunt because it will cross wetlands. But his physical health is only one indication of what he lacks. When he goes for an extended visit to the Hunter farm and is given an empty cotton storehouse for privacy, a nervous George invites the family's younger son, John, to stay with him.

In the early chapters, Uncle James serves as his nephew's guide. But the two-dimensional James is an awkward figure who offers lectures rather than conversation, facts rather than comfort, and advice rather than challenge. Condit must have realized the inadequacy of this chilly, distant figure, who largely disappears from the story after the first chapter. Eventually, about a third of the way through the book, George's uncle disappears entirely, leaving on a convenient business trip for most of the rest of the story. His excursion to New Orleans allows his nephew to continue growing under a far more effective mentor. While this absence might simply reflect the adolescent dream of the disappearance of familial authority, it also gives George a chance to prove himself with adults and peers who have no assumptions about him.

Unlike Uncle James, the eponymous Mr. Hunter is an ideal mentor for this city mouse in the country, a young man who enters the unknown, the wilderness, to find himself. The Florida settler steps in to provide direction just as the young New Yorker begins coming to terms with this new world. Many of the most interesting parts of the book involve George's visits to the Hunters' farm and this wise older role model's stories about his adventures, stories which extend George's imagination and his awareness of what life can involve.

Mr. Hunter both tests and evaluates his young guest. When George wants to go on a night hunt, his host takes him outside to try his skill. After George seems to miss a reasonable shot, his guide criticizes him and explains why he missed. But Mr. Hunter is equally proud of George for deferring a chance to shoot a deer to a younger companion, for killing his first deer on his own, and for the initiatives George takes around the farm. The more the young man is tested, the more he learns and grows.

The Hunters also introduce George to the life of ordinary people who need to go to work regularly in their fields, negotiate for cattle, attend makeshift religious and social events, and cooperate with and rely on neighbors. During his stay on the farm, George grows from an inexperienced young man to a skilful companion on adventures. The boy who feared sleeping alone becomes a young man who mentors the Hunters' boys, learns to feel at home alone in the woods, and finds ways to repay his hosts. He not only builds a new path from the Hunters' house to the main road, a clear symbol of the new path he has fashioned for himself, he also designs and builds a fence for their house and garden, emblematic of his growing ability to help protect others.

The key to George's maturation occurs on his hunts, which graduate in significance and danger from shooting ducks to searching for bear. As his encounters with animals in the wild become increasingly more challenging, they allow him to gain a deeper sense of identity with his new environment. Preparing for his trip south on the opening pages, he thinks about hunting as a recreational activity in which the prey are simply objects. Like Coleridge's ancient mariner, however, the more carefully he examines that new world, the more fully alive it becomes and the more he finds himself developing bonds with other species.

As in much of George's personal development, Mr. Hunter provides a catalytic role in this expansion of his sympathies and imagination. When George and David first visit the Hunters, their host tells them a story of his wrestling match with a massively antlered buck. During the story in Chapter III, Mr. Hunter calls his opponent "Mr. Buck" and, in describing him with personal rather than impersonal pronouns, presents the battle as an epic struggle between two relatively equally matched opponents: "I partly dodged him, caught him by the beams of his horns, and threw my whole weight on his neck, thinking I would get him down and hold him, until my dogs came." That battle would appear very different if the narrator substituted "it" and "its" for "him" and "his," distancing and objectifying the buck.

When his faithful dog, Old Sam, finally comes to help finish the fight with the now one-antlered buck, Sam becomes an almost human partner: "Then the old fellow came to me wagging his tail and licking the blood off his chops, and looked as if he wanted to know if I was hurt. I tell you I had to hug that dog." While his dogs hold a special place in his heart, Mr. Hunter's stories individualize almost all of the animals he encounters. And he sees them as far more than food or sport. After describing that fight with the buck, he discusses the challenges of trying to raise a fawn in an account that sounds a little like an early draft of Marjorie Kinnan Rawling's *The Yearling*.

All of Mr. Hunter's stories about hunting deer, bear, panthers, and alligators reflect his respect for and sense of a connection with his prey. He will quickly eliminate predators that attack his food supplies or make life around the farm more dangerous, but he never loses his admiration for them. His stories also tend to reveal a good deal about human nature among his neighbors. The search for a crooked-footed buck shows the way human rivalries and jealousies crop up even at the edge of the Florida frontier. And his tale of a heroic bear standing up to a party of hunters and withstanding attack after attack ends when Mr. Hunter needs to restrain the local parson, frustrated at the bear's endurance, from leaping on it with a knife in his bloodthirsty rage.

That humanizing influence becomes quickly apparent in George when the young Northerner, soon after hearing these tales, demonstrates some ambivalence about shooting a bear, which he calls "poor Bruin," on his return from a logging camp: "As to killing it, he felt very pleased at having a hand in the hunt, although he did not think it was a thing to brag of as they had every advantage of the poor creature." In much the same spirit, George thinks it a pity to kill graceful squirrels; and watching a cow being manhandled into his friend Captain Ambler's schooner, he calls it "the poor beast" and "the poor brute."

As George learns more about his new world, his empathy grows. While hunting, he never approves of killing just for the sake of killing. But he also understands that almost everything shot becomes food, from venison steaks to squirrel pie. Toward the end of the story, as his ability to identify with even his most dangerous prey expands, he describes an alligator he wants to punish for daring to threaten him in almost familiar terms as "that fellow."

By teaching George admiration and a limited affection for all life, Mr. Hunter provides him with a remarkably humane understanding of frontier life. In that world animals deserve respect, although human rights, both for food and for safety, will always prevail. When the teenager finally manages to kill a deer on his own during another visit to the Hunters in Chapter VIII, "he felt almost sorry that he had shot it." But he accepts the principle of a hierarchy among species, believing that "animals were made for man's use" and knowing that all of his deer would eventually become food or clothing. For Condit, a hierarchy exists among all species. At the top are those who aid humans, like the prized hunting dogs, and those whose size or courage make them notable foes. At the bottom are varmints who raid food supplies or threaten life.

That philosophy may well be why the book's hunting dogs, like many of the animals who are hunted, often have more personality than many of the people George meets. The wily Old Sam who eventually gets eaten by alligators, David's squirrel-hunter Pat who gets perfumed by a skunk, the relentlessly quiet Dragon, the ill-fated Old Caesar, and the eager young Ruler all play critical roles in either hunts or stories. Even Mr. Hunter's mare, the skittish, mischievous Nelly, is a stronger and more developed character than most of the novel's humans.

Mrs. Morton and Mrs. Hunter, for example, do little more than admire, fret, or provide food, while the Hunters' sons, James and John, simply and almost word-lessly let George lead them. Other farmers, like Mr. Pierce, Mr. Lyndale, and the nervous Mr. Bliss, make up hunting parties but do little more. Aside from Mr. Hunter and his dogs, the other three most interesting characters in the countryside may well be the farmer's Revolutionary War musket, his rifle, Danger, and his shotgun, Rattlesnake.

George's Welaka friends have a little more life, especially the logical David, who usually offers scientific explanations for odd experiences, like why George catches more fish than he or the captain. The genial Captain Ambler is a jolly, generous, constantly accommodating companion while he waits for his cattle to arrive; and Captain Stebbins is a practical adult with lots of stories of the Indian Wars. Many of the others serve, as do Mr. Hunter's neighbors, only as background. Some never even earn full names, like the local doctor and General H. Oddest of all is the young man who joins George and David on a number of adventures, an apparent peer of theirs whom the author curiously refers to only as Mr. Hastings. The formal address and lack of biographical background make him an even more shadowy figure than the others.

One of the novel's best figures is a comic one, the boastful, inept guide Hirly, who takes the boys on a deer hunt when George returns from his long stay at the Hunters. Although he appears only briefly at the end of the tenth and the beginning of the eleventh chapters, he becomes the antithesis of what George aspires to be. Hirly, as the narrator, in an unusual ironic comment, tells us, "pretended to be a great hunter" but sends misleading trumpet signals, complains about not having a horse because of his leaky boat, and shows a marked talent for creating excuses when he fails to find any turkeys for dinner. In a world which respects skill and competence, George, after his visits to the Hunters, now shows himself far more skillful and competent than the professional guide.

Despite George's growth, he is still young enough to daydream. On his last outing at the Hunters, for example, George sits on a log and fantasizes: "And this was his last hunt—he felt a little melancholy to think he must give up this free sort of life, and return to the habits and customs of city life. He was really having some vague ideas of giving up all the prospects and plans which he and his friends had formed for his future, and coming to Florida to settle."

Early in the novel the author's voice often breaks into his narrative to provide everything from stern warnings about the dangers for young boys of running off to sea to editorial asides about setting fishing lures. Once he finds Mr. Hunter, he generally allows the story to tell itself with this alter ego's stories providing the adult perspective. George's daydream, however, brings out the author's need once again to speak directly to his audience with only the slightest hint of melancholy: "He only saw the romance of a life in the woods. The novelty of them had not yet worn off and he was an enthusiast though so young"

EDITING

Like most early drafts, the original manuscript of *A Trip to Florida for Health and Sport* has a fairly casual attitude towards writing, with a good deal of repetition, a cavalier view of punctuation and grammar, and a number of inconsistencies. Our primary concern has been to preserve the original's substance, style and tone, while correcting the most obvious and distracting problems. Although we have generally broken up run-on sentences, for example, we have at the same time kept the occasional shifts of narrative, as when the author uses either the first or second person to speak directly to his reader. Those avuncular passages tend to be clustered early in the story, and appear only rarely after Mr. Hunter enters the novel.

To offer a clear sense of the manuscript's punctuation and syntax, we have preserved George's letters to his mother in Chapters II and IV and the excerpt from his diary in Chapter VIII exactly as they appear in the original. In addition to showing the author's loose approach to everything from commas to repetition, those passages capture the voice (and grammar) of a high spirited teenager. We have also left in some of George's—or the author's—occasionally telegraphic passages. Our only significant changes in these sections occur in the diary when the author occasionally forgets that those passages are George's first-person accounts and, while reporting dialogue, writes "asked George" rather than "I asked."

Condit's punctuation tends to be rhetorical rather than traditional. His commas, semicolons and hyphens usually indicate pauses for effect rather than follow any standard usage of mid-nineteenth century American English. Of course, those standards were still working their way into general use. When Harvard awarded President Andrew Jackson, who had been Florida's first American military governor, an honorary doctorate in 1833, John Quincy Adams, a Harvard alumnus and Jackson's predecessor as president, complained that it was wrong to honor an illiterate like Andy Jackson and pointed out that Old Hickory often spelled the same word different ways. Hearing his political rival Adams's comment, Jackson reportedly answered, "It is a damn poor mind indeed which can't think of at least two ways to spell any word."

We thought it especially important to preserve, as fully as possible, the author's language, which often has the rhythm and indirect sensitivity of Victorian American prose—"As the dogs swept past him with their tongues lolling out, George was aware of a singular feeling of faintness coming over him and sank down on the grass"—as well as a tendency towards the formality of his age. In discussions with his very proper Uncle James, for example, George never uses contractions. As a result, their conversations, like this one from the opening chapter, are always a little stiff:

> "I do not exactly understand how a propeller works," said George. They call them screw steamships; it is not a screw that makes us go, is it?"
>
> "You have seen sailors scull a boat, have you not?"
>
> . . . .
>
> 'But are not the side wheel ships much faster?"

That stiffness remains during George's early adventures. On his first trout fishing expedition, his language stays remarkably proper even when he becomes excited: "Oh! I have got – no *stop the boat*! It is a snag." George is nothing if not adaptive, however, so he feels more comfortable using contractions while speaking with the less formally educated Floridians. Although he uses far fewer contractions than locals like Mr. Hunter, George's speech becomes slightly more informal and colloquial when his uncle is not present.

In fact, just as Uncle James's absences generally improve the story, they also perk up the narrative and the dialogue. The formality of the language and Uncle James' interest in edification are largely why their conversations are more stilted than George's adventures in Welaka which capture the excitement of the hunt or the comforts of comradeship. And whenever Uncle James is present, the author seems to adopt his tone in describing Savannah and St. Augustine or offering advice to the reader.

Like Uncle James, a number of other characters have a distinctive rhetoric. Mr. Hunter's vigorous, direct language communicates a sense of immediacy and a frank admiration for achievement. George's two peers can be distinguished by their syntax. David regularly offers rational explanations for odd occurrences in carefully balanced, occasionally complex sentences, while the relatively taciturn Mr. Hastings only speaks to ask fairly simple questions. On the other hand, the unreliable guide Hirly gives the author a chance to try comic Southern dialogue, as when he tells the boys he "had seed lots of bar." Bears often seem to evoke the author's interest in dialect. When General H's slaves are rowing the boys back to Welaka, one of them, Uncle Jack, becomes excited when he sees a bear: "Look dah. See de bar swimmin' over de river."

Even though the book's primarily workmanlike prose ranges from the slightly didactic in the descriptions of Savannah and St. Augustine to uncomplicated adventure narrative, the author does on occasion try to create more striking stylistic effects. He will, for example, invert a sentence to suggest a memorable moment, as when a fire box unexpectedly topples out of a boat into the water in the second chapter: "Furious were the exclamations of surprise and vexation, but they finally ended in a hearty laugh." And he occasionally peppers Mr. Hunter's speech with words like "ferverous" and "boolging."

In addition to Mr. Hunter's vivid stories, there are moments of poetic description, one of the most effective of which occurs in the next to last chapter when George visits St. Augustine's beach:

> Who does not love to stroll upon the beach, where the breakers come dashing on in long lines of foam and cast themselves with an expiring effort upon the sandy beach? Wave follows wave with unremitting constancy and regularity. While they look so great and fierce where they first break into foam, they are shorn of their might as they proceed. And when at last they break and scatter on the sands, they glide hurriedly back as if to seek the shelter of the next wave and ride themselves beneath its advancing foam. And how far will one wander without knowing it. You look forward and think there are some beautiful shells just beyond, on that next point; you reach it, find a few and see more still further on; and so you keep going, stopping to see the waves dash upon each point, until you are astonished as you look at your time piece to see how the hours have gone. And so it was with most of the party.

In addition to standardizing most of the punctuation and grammar, much of our editing involved eliminating repetition. The author has a curious fondness for certain verbs, adjectives, and adverbs. "Very," for example, appears at least four times on ten of the manuscript's first 62 pages, and forms of "commence" over 40 times, three of them on one page. Although we have kept a number of repetitions to capture the original's tone—"furiously," for example, occurs four times in Chapter VI but only three other times in the entire novel—we have pruned some repetition if it seemed intrusive and did not appear important in revealing a character's speech patterns.

When the syntax became too repetitive or redundant, we added conjunctions, transitional phrases or combined sentences. On a few occasions, we shifted material to clarify the story. For example, the author has Mr. Hunter tell a story about using a yager ball in hunting a bear with the bloodthirsty Parson in Chapter IV, but he waits until Chapter IX to explain the origin of the Cuban yagers. We simply moved that explanation forward.

WORKS CITED

John James Audubon. *Ornithological Biography; or, An Account of the Habits of the Birds of the United States.* Vol 2. Edinburgh: A. Black, 1834.

William Bartram. *Travels through North and South Carolina, Georgia, East and West Florida. Philadelphia:* James and Johnson, 1791.

Ledyard Bill. A Winter in Florida: *Observations on the Soil, Climate, and Products of Our Semi-Tropical State; with Sketches of the Principal Towns and Cities in Eastern Florida; to which is added A Brief Historical Summary; together with Hints to the Tourist, Invalid, and Sportsman.* New York: Wood and Holbrook, 1869.

Robert Montgomery Bird. *The Adventures of Robin Day.* 2 vols. Philadelphia: Lea & Blanchard, 1839.

-----. *Nick of the Woods, or, The Jibbenainosay, a Tale of Kentucky.* Philadelphia: Carey, Lea & Blanchard, 1837.

-----. Rpt. *Nick of the Woods.* New York: J.W. Lovell, 1852.

Ned Buntline (Edward Zane Carroll Judson). Matanzas; or, a Brother's Revenge. New York: G.H. Williams, 1848.

--. *The Red Revenger; or, The Pirate King of the Floridas.* New York: Samuel French, 1847.

Alvar Núñez Cabeza de Vaca. *Relación y comentarios del Governador Alvar Núñez Cabeza de Vaca (Los Naufragios).* Valladolid: Francisco Fernández de Cordova, 1555.

Don Pedro Casender [Rev. Michael Smith]. *The Lost Virgin of the South; a Tale of Truth connected with the History of the Indian War in the South.* Tallahassee: M. Smith, 1831.

Mark Catesby. *The Natural History of Carolina, Florida, and the Bahama Islands.* London, 1731-43.

François René de Chateaubriand. *Atala, ou, Les amours de deux sauvages, dans le desert.* Paris: Migneret, 1801.

James Fenimore Cooper. *Jack Tier; or, The Florida Reef.* New York: Burgess, Stinger, 1848.

Frederick Dau. *Florida Old and New.* New York: G.P. Putnam's Sons, 1934.

Daniel Defoe. *Robinson Crusoe*. London: W. Taylor, 1719.

Sarah Stickney Ellis. *My Brother; or, The Man of Many Friends*. London: Sampson, Low, 1855.

Ralph Waldo Emerson. *Journals 1820-1872*. Vol. II (1824-1832). Ed. Edward Waldo Emerson and Waldo Emerson Forbes. Boston: Houghton Mifflin, 1909.

Francis Robert Goulding. *Robert and Harold; or, The Young Marooners on the Florida Coast*. Philadelphia: W.S. Martien, 1853.

----------------------------. *The Soldier's Hymn Book*. Charleston, S.C.: South Carolina Tract Society, 1863.

Lafcadio Hearn. "Floridian Reveries." *Leaves from the Diary of an Impressionist: Early Writings*. Boston: Houghton Mifflin, 1911.

Caroline Lee Hentz. *Marcus Warland; or, The Long Moss Spring: A Tale of the South*. Philadelphia: A. Hart, 1852.

----------. *The Planter's Northern Wife*. Philadelphia: T.B. Peterson and Brothers, 1854.

William Henry Herbert. *Ringwood the Rover*. Philadelphia: W.H. Graham, 1843.

John Howison. "The Florida Pirate." *Blackwood's Edinburgh Magazine* 9 (April – August 1821), 125-31, 305-12, 407-14, 516-31.

Thomas Hutchins. *An Historical Narrative and Topographical Description of Louisiana and West Florida*. Philadephia: [Thomas Hutchins], 1784.

Joseph Holt Ingraham. *Rafael; or, The Twice Condemned. A Tale of Key West*. Boston: H.L. Williams, 1845.

John Beauchamp Jones. *The Winkles*. New York: Appleton, 1855.

Carolyn Keene. *The Clue of the Black Keys*. New York: Grosset & Dunlap, 1951

Sidney Lanier. *Florida: Its Scenery, Climate, and History*. Philadelphia: J.B. Lippincott, 1876.

Henry Wadsworth Longfellow. *The Song of Hiawatha*. Boston: Ticknor and Fields, 1855.

William Bernard MacCabe. *Florine, Princess of Bergundy: A Tale of the First Crusades*. Baltimore: John Murphy, 1855.

Peter Martyr d'Anghiera. *De Orbe Novo Decades*. Compluti: apud Mich. De Equia, 1530.

Herman Melville. *Benito Cereno. Putnam's Monthly* 6.34 (October), 353-367; 6.35 (November), 459-474; 6.35 (December), 633-644. 1855.

John Muir. *A Thousand Mile Walk to the Gulf.* Boston and New York: Houghton Mifflin, 1916.

James Burchett Ransom. *Osceola; or, Fact and Fiction: A Tale of the Seminole War.* New York: Harper & Brothers, 1838

Marjorie Kinnan Rawlings. *The Yearling.* New York: C. Scribner's Sons, 1938.

Jean Ribaut. *The Whole and True Discoverye of Terra Florida (Englished the Florishing Lande).* London: Rouland Hall for Thomas Hacket, 1563.

William Roberts. *An Account of the First Discovery and Natural History of Florida.* London: T. Jefferys, 1763.

Bernard Romans. *A Concise Natural History of East and West Florida.* New York: [Bernard Romans], 1775.

William Shakespeare. *The Tempest.* c.1610-11.

William Gilmore Simms. *The Lily and the Totem: The Huguenots in Florida.* New York: Baker and Scribner, 1850.

------------------------------. *Vasconselos:A Romance of the New World.* New York: Redfield Co, 1853.

Claudia Slate, Steve Glassman, eds. *Florida Studies: Proceedings of the 2006 Annual Meeting of the Florida College English Association.* Newcastle: Cambridge Scholars Publishing, 2007.

Claudia Slate, Keith Huneycutt, eds. *Florida Studies: Proceedings of the 2007 Annual Meeting of the Florida College English Association.* Newcastle upon Tyne: Cambridge Scholars Press, 2008.

Emma Dorothy Eliza Nevitte Southworth. *The Missing Bride; or, Miriam the Avenger.* Philadelphia: T.B. Peterson, 1855.

Harriet Beecher Stowe. *Palmetto Leaves.* Boston: Houghton, Mifflin, 1873.

Silvia Sunshine. *Petals Plucked from Sunny Climes.* Nashville: Southern Methodist Publishing House, 1879.

Walt Whitman. *Leaves of Grass.* Brooklyn, NY: [Walt Whitman], 1855.

Johann David Wyss. *Swiss Family Robinson.* Philadelphia: Porter & Coates, 18--.